Zebras are highly social, living in groups consisting of several mares accompanied by a stallion.

NATURE FACTS
MAMMALS

Young baboons grooming one another. This activity is an
important way of reinforcing social bonding in these primates.

Tigers are solitary creatures. A male will not encourage a female to enter his territory unless she is in breeding condition and even then they only stay together for about two weeks.

NATURE FACTS

MAMMALS

DAVID ALDERTON

Grange
BOOKS

Published by Grange Books
An imprint of Grange Books Limited
The Grange
Grange Yard
London
SE1 3AG

Reprinted 1993
CLB 2587
© 1992 CLB Publishing, Godalming, Surrey
All rights reserved
Printed and bound in Italy by New Interlitho
ISBN 1-85627-339-3

The Author
David Alderton has had a life-long interest in wildlife. Since graduating from Cambridge University, his work as a specialist writer on animals has enabled him to travel far afield, observing many creatures in their natural habitats. David also attends various international meetings where conservation matters are discussed, and he is acutely aware of the difficulties faced by many species today in their constant battle for survival. David has written many books on a range of animal-orientated subjects, and he is a regular contributor to various general and specialist publications on natural history topics. He has also taken part in radio and TV programmes.

Credits
Edited and designed: Ideas into Print
Layouts: Stonecastle Graphics Ltd.
Picture Editors: Annette Lerner, John Kaprielian
Photographs: Photo Researchers Inc., New York
Commissioning Editor: Andrew Preston
Production: Ruth Arthur, Sally Connolly, David Proffit, Andrew Whitelaw
Director of Production: Gerald Hughes
Typesetting: Ideas into Print Ltd.
Colour Separations: Scantrans Pte. Ltd., Singapore

The female bear gives birth to up to four cubs. They remain with her for at least a year and she defends them fiercely against intruders.

CONTENTS

The success of mammals

In common with many other mammals, zebras have a keen sense of sight as well as acute hearing. Zebras typically live in herds to protect themselves against predators that roam on the plains.

As the era of the dinosaurs drew to a close, about 65 million years ago, small creatures – the forerunners of today's mammals – were already established on the planet. Since then, this group has evolved into the dominant life force. There are less than 5,000 species of mammals alive today – a low number compared with invertebrates, for example – but their adaptability is beyond doubt. They vary in size from tiny shrews, just 35mm(1.4in) long excluding their tail, and weighing 1.5gm(0.053oz), up to gigantic blue whales, which can grow to at least 28m(92ft) long

Small mammals, like shrews, often have a high reproductive rate and a short lifespan.

Zebras reproduce at a slow rate; only one calf is born after a gestation of nearly a year.

Suckling is vital. The first milk, called colostrum, contains protective antibodies that help the youngster fight off infections.

and weigh 140 tonnes (308,700lb). Unlike reptiles and fish, mammals have been freed from a dependence on environmental temperature to regulate body activity. They are described as endotherms, being able to maintain body temperature independently of their surroundings, but this does not mean that all mammals have the same body temperature. The primitive monotremes have an average temperature of just 30°C(86°F), compared to 39°C(102.33°F) in rabbits. Mammals have been able to colonize much of the earth, even venturing successfully into the

Humpback whales may live for 50 years or more, but are slow to mature and reproduce.

A vervet monkey with her young male offspring and a suckling infant. Maternal concern in mammals is often most evident in the primates.

their chances of survival, and so mammals produce relatively few offspring. In the great apes, where the offspring are born relatively helpless, the young are nurtured and taught by their parents, who pass on essential lessons of survival from one generation to the next. Being born into a herd fulfils the same function. The matriarch of an elephant herd, for example, may be too old to breed successfully, but can still help to ensure the survival of the group by using her knowledge of their territory. Other factors have also contributed to the rise of the mammals. They have evolved relatively large brains, reflecting their complex range of senses. Sight and sound are vital to most species, while scent is also significant, not only for locating food, but also in territorial situations. Taste is less well developed. Body hair provides both insulation and camouflage, as in the arctic fox, which grows a thicker, white coat in winter, and by moulting their hair regularly, mammals can adjust their heat output. Hair has also taken on sensory functions and certain hairs have developed into whiskers, normally on the head, but sometimes on the feet. Fat is also important, especially in mammals living in polar areas; it provides further insulation and also acts as a valuable store of energy.

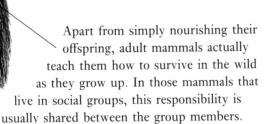

Apart from simply nourishing their offspring, adult mammals actually teach them how to survive in the wild as they grow up. In those mammals that live in social groups, this responsibility is usually shared between the group members.

A female grey squirrel with her offspring. Rodents typically have a short gestation period and their young are often born blind and helpless.

polar regions, where reptiles would not be able to survive, let alone reproduce. Another reason why the group has spread and diversified to such a great extent is the high degree of parental care given by mammals to their offspring. No longer are the young left to fend for themselves, even while they are developing from the egg. Instead, they can be born in an advanced state and, in the case of many herbivores, virtually ready to run alongside their mother. This greatly improves

The evolution of mammals

The elephant of today bears a distinct resemblance to its extinct relative, the mammoth. The variation in body hair reflects their differing environments.

Since mammals first appeared on the earth, many species have developed and then died out as part of the evolutionary process. Many of the species found today had much larger ancestors in the past. They became extinct and were replaced by smaller individuals. This pattern can be clearly seen in one of the oldest groups of mammals still represented on the planet. The discovery of the fossilized remains of armadillos, sloths and anteaters has enabled man to trace back their family tree over 40 million years. At that time, a group of huge armadillos, called the glyptodonts has already developed. Their bodies were basically similar to the armadillos of today, but had become so large, measuring about 2.5m(just over 8ft) long, that they could not curl up into a ball. Their heads were well-protected, however, and their flexible tails were armed with vicious spikes. By swinging the tail from side to side, these giant armadillos could inflict a serious injury on a potential predator. Nevertheless, the line finally died out about one million years ago. In the sloths, a giant form evolved about two million years ago called *Megatherium*. Unlike their modern descendants, these mammals were too big to live in the trees, but at 6m(20ft) tall, they were able to reach into the branches. In contrast, the anteaters, the most recent branch of the family to

Mammoth tusks were similar to those of elephants. They are still unearthed in the far north and used for ivory carving.

have emerged, only appear to have reached their maximum size today. The largest recorded species is the giant anteater from South America, which measures about 1m (39in) long in the body, with a slightly shorter tail.

Elephants are another group that showed much greater diversity in their appearance in the past. Mammoths in the far north stood up to 4m(13ft) tall, with tusks of similar length and shaggy hair to conserve body heat in the cold environment. Other types of elephant had much shorter tusks, but elongated mouths. Predatory mammal species could also grow much larger, enabling them to

The early ancestors of elephants arose in Africa about 55 million years ago. As these creatures evolved, they moved into Asia and the Americas when the landmasses were more closely connected than today. The different branches of the family then evolved in relative isolation.

Mammoths moved to the edge of the Arctic, and developed a thick coat to protect them from the cold.

The specialist feeding habits of the giant panda make it vulnerable to environmental change.

The big concern, especially in the larger mammals, is to ensure that they retain adequate habitat, otherwise the giant panda and other species will die out.

prey on mammoths and other giant herbivores. Probably the best-known are the so-called sabre-toothed tigers, with vicious, long canine teeth in their upper jaws. These may have been used to inflict a fatal bite through the spinal cord or to wrestle prey down to the ground. Such cats had become extinct about 11,000 years ago. By that stage, many of the large species on which they preyed had also died out, and it seems likely that these large, bulky cats were less able to hunt and catch smaller, more agile prey. As a result, other cats better suited to this lifestyle began to thrive and became the dominant carnivores in some areas.

It is not clear why mammoths died out. They may have been heavily hunted by early man.

The sabre-tooth tiger's huge canine teeth were used like daggers on prey animals.

Today, the dentition of the tiger is far less specialized, as in this Indian tiger, but there is still a slight enlargement of the canines.

Man and mammals

Early man hunted animals for food, but as he adopted a more settled lifestyle about 10,000 years ago, he discovered the benefits of keeping animals rather than hunting them. Although this was more labour intensive, there was a guarantee of food that could be taken when needed. The history of domestication dates back to at least 7000 BC, when sheep known as the mouflon - a species that still survives in the wild - were kept by Neolithic farmers in Asia. Sheep not only supplied meat, but milk and wool as well. Less than 3,000 years later, the effects of domestication could be clearly seen in contemporary paintings, which confirmed that ewes had lost their horns and their fleece had

become more woolly. Goats were soon showing a similar reduction in height. The auroch, or wild ox, was the original ancestor of all the domestic breeds of cattle in the world, but hunting pressures meant that it had finally became extinct early in the 1600s. The Egyptians appear to have been the first people to keep cattle for milk, meat and as a source of hides. Cattle have also been used for ploughing. Pigs are descended from wild boar and are easy to keep, which has encouraged their domestication. By Roman times, two distinct forms of the pig had evolved. Forest pigs were much smaller than their wild ancestor and were allowed to forage for their own food. A larger and much fatter breed of pig was kept in a sty and fed on scraps. Not

An American Indian on horseback in the southwestern USA. Horses were brought to North America barely 500 years ago.

Before the advent of mechanized transport, horses played a vital role in moving men and materials.

The bridle enables the rider to control his horse easily and safely.

Horses are not instinctively prepared to allow themselves to be fitted with tack, and some actively resent it even to the extent of rearing up.

Teams of bullocks in Thailand may work long hours ploughing the land. The sure-footed oxen also move heavy goods, journeying along primitive tracks without difficulty.

A Bedouin boy minds the family herd of camels. Where other transport is not available, these animals represent a secure investment, despite their difficult behaviour.

All domestic dogs are thought to be descended from the grey wolf. These racing sled dogs belong to the spitz group and typically have curly tails.

all animals were domesticated primarily as a source of food, however, although this is why horses were first kept. The process began in what is now the Ukraine, in about 4350 B.C., but horses were not used for riding until 1600 B.C. Farmers first kept dogs to guard their flocks and dogs were probably domesticated in different parts of the world at about the same time, bearing in mind the wide distribution of the grey wolf. There is no clear evidence to confirm when cats were originally kept, but the process probably began in the Middle East. In time, cats were regarded as valuable allies, killing rodents that attacked grain stores. A variety of animals have been domesticated around the world, including camels, guinea pigs, chinchillas, dormice and water buffalo. However, it is important to distinguish between those that have been selectively bred over many generations by human design and, say, the Asiatic elephant or various deer that have been kept, often semi-wild, as working animals or for food. They have yet to be altered by controlled breeding for particular features – the definition of an animal that is fully domesticated.

Cats are easier to cater for than dogs and make popular pets. There are over 50 different cat breeds and many more colour forms to choose from.

Egglaying mammals — curious relics from the past?

Although 34 teeth begin to develop in the young platypus, only 12 break through the gums, to be replaced by horny ridges.

Of all the mammals, the egglayers found in Australia and parts of New Guinea, are probably the strangest. The group consists of just the duckbilled platypus and two species of echidna, also described collectively as monotremes. Their origins are unknown, but on the evidence of their method of reproduction they have certainly existed for at least 15 million years. The monotremes are the only mammals to lay eggs. Each soft-shelled egg measures about 15mm in diameter and 17mm long (0.5x0.7in), and only one or two are normally produced. In echidnas, incubation is carried out in a special pouch on the abdomen and lasts about ten days. The female platypus, on the other hand, nests in a burrow as much as 30m(100ft) long and hatches her eggs simply by curling around them for this period. The young are almost totally helpless when they hatch, and baby platypuses remain concealed in their burrows until they are nearly four months old. Echidnas stay in their mother's pouch for the first two months, but then she leaves them in burrows while she continues to hunt for ants and termites. She returns at intervals to suckle her young for a further four weeks or so, and after that they are left to forage on their own. Platypuses feed strictly under water, using their peculiar bill to locate crayfish, worms and similar invertebrates. Once its cheek pouches are full, the platypus swims back to the surface and chews its food, using special horny plates rather than teeth. It weighs about 2.4kg(5lb) and needs about half its body weight in food every day.

Having broken open a termite mound with its sharp claws, the echidna, or spiny anteater, feeds on termites and other insects, using its sticky, narrow tongue.

16

The webbing on the platypus's forelegs extends beyond the tips of the digits. It comes up to breathe every minute or so, but can remain under water for up to 15 minutes if danger threatens. Males are larger than females.

The body temperature of monotremes is lower than that of other mammals, averaging 30°C(86°F). During hibernation, it can fall to just 4°C(39°F).

❏ When the skin of a platypus was first brought to Europe in 1798, it was assumed to be a fake, manufactured from the beak of a duck and the fur of a small mammal.

❏ The bill of the platypus gives off slight electrical charges. These, and the bill's sensitive nerve endings, enable the platypus to locate food under water, even though its eyes and ears are closed.

❏ The platypus possesses a deadly surprise, in the form of spurs on its hind legs. These are connected directly to venom glands that produce a poison strong enough to kill a dog and paralyze a man's leg. The reason for this protection is unclear. Echidnas also have these spurs, which measure about 1.25cm(0.5in) long, but they do not inject poison with them. Females of the platypus and both species of echidna lose these spurs during the first year of their lives.

❏ Monotremes, such as the echidna pictured above, rapidly burrow down to escape land temperatures that can reach 40°C(104°F) in certain parts of their natural range.

Koalas – cute but not cuddly

Another example of Australia's strange wildlife, the koala 'bear', is found only on the eastern side of the country. It is not a bear but a marsupial, with a pouch like kangaroos in which the young are reared from a very early stage in their development. Koalas have a highly specialized diet, feeding almost exclusively on the leaves and bark of eucalyptus trees. The koala's digestive tract has become modified, with a population of beneficial bacteria present in their greatly enlarged caecum. These microorganisms help to break down the often toxic eucalyptus leaves, so they can be digested properly. Koalas spend virtually their entire lives in the trees. Their feet are well adapted for climbing and resting in the tree tops and they have little fear of falling. These marsupials lead solitary lives and males establish quite large territories that can extend over an area of 3 hectares (7.4 acres). At breeding time, in particular, they can become aggressive and maintain their territories by calling loudly to intimidate potential rivals. They also mark trees using a scent produced from a special gland on the chest. Baby koalas are born about 35 days after mating, and each will spend the next five months or so in its mother's pouch. The youngster remains with her for up to a year, often clinging onto her back as she climbs about. Koalas face few natural enemies, although the fires that periodically sweep through the Australian bush take a toll on their numbers.

The young koala's sharp claws help it to cling to its mother. It leaves the pouch at about five months, by which time it will have grown 18cm(7in) long.

A female gives birth every second year. The single baby measures less than 2.5cm (1in) at birth, but its forelimbs are strong, enabling it to climb into the pouch.

Out of about 350 different types of eucalyptus, koalas depend on just six as sources of food.

All koalas can sleep as long as 18 hours each day. They wake up at intervals to feed, eating a larger meal at dusk.

Koalas do not suffer from parasites, such as lice. The eucalyptus oil on their fur acts as a natural insecticide.

Koalas can survive long periods without water, as they extract sufficient from the eucalyptus leaves. 'Koala' is derived from an Aboriginal word meaning 'no drink'.

Koalas are not generally disturbed by the presence of people. This made them an easy target for hunters who wanted their fur.

Kangaroos and wallabies – designed to hop

An eastern grey kangaroo, its tail held out as a counterbalance as it hops.

The second and third toes are partially fused with skin, and the first toe is absent. The legs themselves are elongated.

This group of about 50 species is not able to walk because the animals' rear legs, which are used for locomotion, cannot operate independently of one another on land. These marsupials must therefore hop, unless they are swimming. Then, with the water supporting the bulk of their body, they can move each hind leg in turn. The long tail serves as a balancing aid, lying on the ground when the animal is resting and carried almost horizontally as it hops along. The kangaroo's forelimbs are greatly shortened but useful for grooming. Males may fight each other with them when they are breeding, inflicting nasty scratches with their sharp claws as they battle for mates. Kangaroos and wallabies are vegetarian. Many species feed primarily on grass and have developed a special method of breaking down this plant material. As in the koala, bacteria perform this function, but there is a special pouch in the stomach for this purpose, rather than lower down in the digestive tract. Young kangaroos and wallabies are born after a remarkably short gestation period of less than five weeks, but they are tiny and helpless. The young of the largest species - the red kangaroo, which can stand up to 2.1m(6ft 8in) tall when adult - weighs just 0.75gm(0.03oz) and is less than 2.5cm(1in) long at birth. After instinctively crawling into its mother's pouch, the baby develops slowly, remaining tightly clasped to the nipple until it is 10 weeks old. The young kangaroo first leaves the security of the pouch when it is nearly six months old, but returns when danger threatens. It will not be completely weaned for a year.

The kangaroo's pouch opens at the front. Inside, there may be four nipples, but only two are likely to be producing milk. Single offspring are most common.

A red-necked wallaby with a 9-month old joey. Their name originates from the Wallaby Islands on the west coast of Australia. They were first recorded in 1629 - before the discovery of Australia itself - by a shipwrecked Dutch sea captain, Francisco Pelsaert. The term 'wallaby' is still used for the smaller members of the group.

Rival male kangaroos battle for mating rights. One tries to immobilize the other using its forelimbs and kicks out at its rival's belly. Injuries are common.

A female may have an older offspring outside her pouch and another developing withir

One of the semi-arboreal tree kangaroos. They are confined to New Guinea, and the northwestern corner of Queensland in Australia.

❑ Kangaroos are able to jump over obstacles that are 3m (10ft) high, and can move forward 12.2m(40ft) at a single bound. They can also travel at speeds of 40kph(25mph).

❑ It was originally thought that the young were born directly into the pouch, rather than crawling there. This method was first suggested in 1830, but not widely accepted until the entire process was observed during 1923. It was filmed for the first time in 1960.

❑ Females mate almost immediately after giving birth, but the embryo does not develop until the older offspring has left the pouch. If that youngster dies at an early stage, it is soon replaced by the fertilized embryo.

❑ The tree kangaroos differ from their terrestrial counterparts in having longer and more powerful forelimbs, while their hind limbs have become shorter. This enables them to climb around in trees without difficulty. Rock wallabies inhabit steep cliff faces and similar areas. They also have shorter hind legs, which they use to maintain a firm grip on the rocks .

❑ The forest wallaby from the rainforest areas of New Guinea has a scaly tip to its tail, which is pushed into the ground as a support when the animal is resting. Its relatively large eyes improve its vision in dim lighting conditions.

Insectivorous mammals – an ancient order

There are over 400 species of insectivore and they vary considerably in appearance and lifestyle. Many, including hedgehogs, live on land but others, such as moles, have adapted to life under the ground. The desmans - shrewlike animals found in Europe and northern Asia - belong to a third category, spending much of their time under water, hunting invertebrates. Each group has evolved superbly to suit its own environment, which is not entirely surprising, since insectivores are considered to be one of the oldest surviving mammalian lines. Their ancestors are thought to be among the earliest mammals to reproduce by means of a placenta, rather than simply by laying eggs. Several characteristics readily distinguish the insectivores. Firstly, they tend to be small, varying from the pygmy white-toothed shrew weighing just 2gm(0.07oz) up to the greater moonrat, which can weigh 1.4kg(3lb).

These active mammals rely more on their sense of smell than on sight to locate their prey. As a result, they have long pointed noses, and many are nocturnal feeders. Because they are small, insectivores generally need a relatively large intake of food to maintain their body temperature. They have a high reproductive rate and a correspondingly short lifespan; shrews, for example, often live less than a year. Shrews, like other insectivores, prefer a solitary lifestyle that avoids direct competition for food. They are the most numerous insectivores, with over 250 species presently known, and also occur over the widest area. Insectivores are found on all continents except Australia, but are only represented in the extreme northwest of South America.

The common shrew has a wide area of distribution, being found in many different habitats right across Europe and Asia, as far as Japan.

The mole's whiskers help it to feel its way through the dark and detect the vibrations of prey in its tunnels.

The common mole's powerful forelegs act like miniature shovels boring through the soil, and the digits also serve as hands, being used to restrain prey.

The hedgehog uses its claws for digging, and possibly to scratch itself, since many are infested with fleas that live on no other animals.

The highly specialized elephant shrew, with its long nose and elongated hind legs, lives only in Africa.

Owls prey on hedgehogs and badgers can stop them curling up.

The streaked tenrec is a native of Madagascar. It may have 40 teeth in its narrow jaws and preys mainly on insects.

The large, fleshy nose of the mole is flexible and sensitive. In one North American species it has become star-shaped and is divided into many fleshy tentacles.

❏ Shrews, such as the common tree shrew above, are nervous and can die of fright. Even the sound of a thunderstorm can prove fatal, pushing up their heartbeat to 1,200 beats per minute, which is 20 beats per second!

❏ The average hedgehog is protected by a covering of about 5,000 sharp spines. Young hedgehogs are born with a smooth body, but their quills erupt very soon after birth. The erectile spines are actually modified hairs.

❏ Some shrews and the rare Caribbean solenodons produce a poisonous saliva, capable of killing prey soon after biting it. It enables the Eurasian water shrew to rapidly subdue fish or frogs that may be bigger than itself.

❏ Moles often maintain a special larder near their nests in which they store the earthworms they catch in their network of tunnels. The worms are killed and eaten later.

❏ In the summer, young moles venture above ground looking for a new habitat. They are very vulnerable at this time and many fall victim to owls.

Bats – hunters of the night

The short-nosed fruit bat feeds on fruit and flowers, especially banana blossoms. It can damage the plants.

Bats are the only mammal group to have developed the ability to fly and they have colonized virtually the entire world, except for the polar regions. A number of species are confined to many of the islands in the Pacific Ocean. These include the flying foxes – the largest of the bats – with a wingspan measuring as much as 1.65m(5.4ft) from tip to tip. The evolution of bats remains something of a mystery, however, because to date little has been discovered about their flying ancestors. It is believed that they could have originated from some insectivorous mammals that spent much of their time hunting for their food in trees and developed the ability to glide in pursuit of flying insects. Today, over three-quarters of the world's 977 species of bats feed on insects, reflecting a likely link with these early gliding mammals. They no longer glide, however, but actually fly by flapping their wings. Most species are nocturnal, leaving their roosts at dusk. Insectivorous bats have evolved a particularly sophisticated system of navigation called echolocation, which enables them to fly and catch prey in total darkness. The bats emit high-pitched sounds – ultrasounds – and use their sensitive ears to pick up the echoes bouncing off nearby objects to build up a 'sound picture' of their environment. Bats also use their eyes; in the flying foxes, for example, they are large and give good visibility in semi-darkness.

Big-eared bats may become caught up by their wings on sharp shrubs as they swoop down in search of their insect prey.

These insectivorous bats can rely on sharp eyes, as well as their echolocation system, to locate prey.

Some insects respond to the bat's ultrasound by dropping at the last moment, hoping to commit the bat to strike, while they fall out of reach.

In fruit-eating bats, such as these flying foxes, seeds pass through the digestive tract intact and may be voided well away from their feeding grounds, giving rise to new plants.

Flight is an instinctive skill. Young bats follow their mother's ultrasounds, tracking her flight path as she travels.

The aptly named fisherman bat skims over the water, detecting fish near the surface and seizing them with its sharp claws. It also takes aquatic insects and crustaceans.

These bats can take off from water if they land there, and can swim if necessary. During the day, they roost in groups in caves or hollow trees.

❏ Most bats are highly social mammals. Some of their roosting sites, often located in caves, may be home to over 40 million individuals.

❏ The three species of vampire bat are dreaded because they feed on blood. Their teeth are specially adapted for this purpose, and their saliva contains a powerful anti-coagulant that prevents their victim's blood from clotting normally while they feed from the wound. As a result of their feeding habits, vampire bats can spread the deadly rabies virus. In those parts of Central and South America where vampire bats are found, up to a million cattle and many people die annually.

❏ Some bats hibernate when food is short; others migrate. European noctule bats, for example, may travel 2,000km (1,200miles) when migrating.

Lemurs – Madagascar's very own species

The crowned lemur is restricted to a small area of woodland in the far north of Madagascar.

These strange relatives of the monkey are found principally on Madagascar, an island off the southwestern coast of Africa, although some are also represented on the tiny Comoros Islands nearby. It is thought that at least 50 million years ago their ancestors originated in Africa and may have crossed to Madagascar on rafts of vegetation. The island separated from Africa 150 million years ago, and the lemur's ancestors may have been present even then. In their new environment, and with few natural predators, the group underwent a major diversification, but deforestation on the island has brought many species of lemur close to extinction. Before this, hunting by the early human settlers, who first reached Madagascar about 2,000 years ago, eliminated the largest members of the group, which were virtually as tall as ourselves. In comparison, the mouse lemurs are the smallest species, and can weigh as little as 50gm(1.25oz). They tend to lead rather solitary lives, but larger lemurs are often seen in troops. Ring-tailed lemurs are among the most conspicuous species, with each troop of up to 30 individuals establishing its own territory. Males have a peculiar spur on each wrist connected to a scent gland and they mark the territory of the troop by cutting into the bark with the spur, leaving a residue of their scent behind. Whereas most lemurs prefer to live in trees, the ring-tail is equally at home on the ground. It feeds mainly on plants and fruits, but may also consume insects, which feature more prominently in the diets of the smaller species.

Female lemurs often share the rearing of their young. Pregnancy lasts about four months and the young are born in March and April.

When walking on the ground, ring-tailed lemurs carry their boldly patterned tails vertically as a signal to other members of the group.

❑ The aye-aye, a close relative of the lemurs, is also found on Madagascar. It feeds mainly on grubs and insects, which it hunts in the bark of trees. It has just a single pair of incisor teeth at the front of its mouth, for chewing off bark. the third finger of each hand is reduced to the thickness of a wire, and is used to extract insects from the bark, as well as for grooming. Ayes-ayes also eat coconuts, scooping out the contents of the nut with this finger, having first chewed a hole through the husk.

❑ In 1987 and again during 1988, zoologists were amazed when two previously unknown species of lemur were discovered on Madagascar. These species have extremely localized areas of distribution, which explains why they had remained hidden for so long. Unfortunately, both are now threatened by the widespread development that is taking place on the island.

❑ Dwarf lemurs are able to store fat at the base of their tails, which become quite swollen. When food is short, this reserve will prevent the lemur from starving.

❑ The hairy-eared dwarf lemur is believed to be the rarest primate in the world. It lives in the rainforests of eastern Madagascar and confirmation of its survival was not obtained until 1989, when the species was sighted in the wild for the first time since 1965.

Sifaka lemurs are active during the day, even at the hottest times. They are very agile, leaping from branch to branch, walking upright or hopping on the ground.

Brown lemurs live in groups of 4 to 15 individuals. An adult female heads each group.

The ruffed lemur was once considered a holy animal that worshipped the sun because of its habit of sunbathing. Now it is threatened.

Twin ruffed lemurs. The young cling to their mother's belly, then climb on her back.

Marmosets and tamarins— the smallest monkeys

These appealing primates inhabit the forest of Central and South America, where they are usually seen in family groups. The pygmy marmoset, which lives in the upper Amazon, weighs just over 100gm(3.5oz), while the critically endangered golden lion tamarin is the biggest member of the group, weighing up to 700gm (24.5oz). These monkeys are highly dependent on areas of tropical rainforest, leaping easily from branch to branch and foraging in the trees for fruit and insects. They raid birds' nests, taking both eggs and chicks, and kill lizards and other small animals by biting the animal's head. Pregnancy lasts about four months and breeding females usually produce twins. Both parents are closely involved in the care of their offspring; the male helps to carry the young about, while his mate will feed them when required. It is now clear that in most troops, older youngsters - especially males - also play a significant part in looking after babies. This may serve as a learning process for the time when they themselves become parents. Most groups consist of more young males than females, because females tend to mature before their male counterparts and leave to join other groups at an earlier stage. It is not uncommon for males to stay with their parents until they are two years old. Their lifespan, at least in captivity, may be at least 15 years. There is considerable communication between these social monkeys, and they are known to have a vocabulary of at least 17 distinct calls. These range from a danger alert to whines that solicit contact with a partner.

Captive breeding is helping to increase tamarin numbers.

If deprived of Vitamin C in their diet, these monkeys develop the symptoms of scurvy. Just like humans, they are unable to manufacture this essential vitamin in their bodies.

The golden lion tamarin is found in the coastal region of southeastern Brazil. These tamarins are so-called because the mane of hair around the neck resembles that of a male lion.

Agility in the tree-tops requires careful judgement and coordination. The common marmoset has the biggest brain of all mammals in proportion to its body weight. Its brain is equivalent to 5.55 percent of its total body weight.

The pygmy marmoset is the smallest of all monkeys - their babies are little bigger than a bean! They are agile climbers, but less able to jump than their larger relatives.

The black-tailed marmoset is a more aggressive hunter than other species, often preying on small animals and birds. It also tends to be found in more open forest, roaming in bands of a dozen or more individuals.

Baboons and mandrills – dog-faced primates

A male mandrill bares his teeth. Mandrills are equipped with fearsome canine teeth and bright blue and red markings on the face.

The seven species of baboon and their close cousin the mandrill all live in Africa, occupying a variety of habitats from open savanna to rocky upland areas. Baboons are social primates that live in troops, possibly made up of over 200 individuals. Within the troop are a number of smaller family units, the basic one being the harem, consisting of a single male and several females, perhaps accompanied by some of the younger males. These may join together with other harems to form a clan numbering, perhaps, 30 baboons. If they join with other clans, then a band is formed, and when two bands link up, the result is a troop. Baboons prefer to forage on the ground for fruit and vegetable matter, locusts and other small creatures. In coastal areas they may forage in rock pools for crabs and similar invertebrates. Sometimes group members cooperate when seeking food. Baboons generally walk on all fours with a kind of rolling motion, but they have been seen chasing hares, which they kill and eat. Within their territory, baboons may cover distances of about 8km(5 miles) daily, resting during the hottest part of the day. Grooming is a popular activity at this time.

A hamadryas baboon. Bolder individuals sample food before the rest of the troop start to feed.

Communication often relies on facial postures. Interestingly, in these monkeys, displaying the teeth is a sign of friendliness and not aggression, as it is in other species. In fact, males display markings on their buttocks as a threat to competing males.

After a gestation period of six months, females usually produce a single youngster. Grooming has an important function, helping to reinforce the social structure in troops.

An olive baboon. This group of monkeys have cheek pouches in which they can store food. They are thus able to make a grab for food and then quickly escape from danger.

Baboon society is based on a clearly defined social hierarchy, with certain males being more 'senior'. These are usually the larger, stronger individuals.

The young baboon's posture alters as it grows older. At first it is carried on its mother's breast, but later it travels on her back, gradually sitting upright.

FACT FILE

❏ Males of these species are the largest of all monkeys, and may weigh up to 59kg(130lb).

❏ Baboons do not walk on the palms of their hands. Instead, they use their finger tips for this purpose, keeping the palm in a vertical position. They often feed on the ground using one limb, while supporting themselves on the other three.

❏ Every month, swellings containing fluid appear around the thighs and rump of female baboons, indicating that they are ready to mate. They may fight each other over a particular male, but battles amongst baboons are rarely very violent encounters. While the animals may show their sharp teeth and lash out at an opponent with their hands, they rarely inflict real injuries.

❏ A baboon called Jack started to operate the signal box near Vitenhage in South Africa on behalf of his owner who lost his legs in an accident. Jack continued working as an official railway company employee for nine trouble-free years, until his death in 1980.

❏ As dusk falls, baboons climb up into the trees, where the group can rest for the night in relative safety.

❏ Baboons have become very cautious about feeding at sites where food may have been baited with poison to deter them from raiding crops.

Chimpanzees – the warring apes

Chimps may use a stick for prodding into a termites' nest to capture some of the insects.

Living in groups that may consist of up to 20 individuals, chimpanzees are often prepared to fight ferociously to defend their territory from intruders. Roaming bands of male chimpanzees are most dangerous, because they will seek to displace the dominant male in a group. Primitive weapons are often used in such encounters, with stones being thrown and sticks employed to beat opponents. Fruit and vegetable matter form the basis of the chimpanzee's diet, but some troops also hunt small game and have been known to kill and eat other primates, such as young baboons. Chimpanzees generally walk on the ground, using their front, as well as their hind legs, but at times they take to the tree-tops, swinging from branch to branch. As night approaches, the chimpanzees start to construct beds of vegetation off the ground, typically at a height of about 10m(30ft), where they will sleep. Each member of the group has its own bed, except for the young chimps, which remain with their mothers. The beds are usually abandoned on the following morning and the chimpanzees move on through their territory, building fresh beds each night. Chimpanzees mature quite slowly and a female may be 14 years old before she is able to breed. Breeding can take place at any time of year, and females normally produce just a single youngster after a gestation period of about 32 weeks. It will be over three years before the young chimpanzee is fully weaned, and it may remain with its mother for over a decade. The family bonds between female chimpanzees are especially strong, and can last for life. Chimps may continue breeding until they are at least 40, and have been known to live for as long as 60 years.

A mother with her baby, just 20 weeks old.

A female chimp with 10-month-old baby. These highly intelligent apes can communicate with people using sign language they have been taught.

An old male, his grey hairs a sign of ageing. Males spend their entire lives in the group where they were born. They face relatively few predators in the wild.

The pygmy chimpanzee has a distinctive black face, but is no smaller than the common chimpanzee.

❏ The facial gestures of chimpanzees are important as a means of communication. Pouting of the lips is a sign of friendly greeting, while a smile revealing the bottom teeth is an indication of pleasure. In contrast, baring the teeth indicates aggressive feelings.

❏ Chimpanzees are the most intelligent of the three great apes, (the others being the orang-utan and gorilla), and are considered to be our nearest relatives in the animal kingdom. When travelling in groups they can communicate using a variety of calls.

❏ Chimpanzees feed off a wide variety of plants and fruits - up to 300 species during the course of a year. They also have large appetites; an adult male chimpanzee may eat 50 bananas in a single meal.

❏ In recent years, the number of chimpanzees has declined greatly. They have now vanished from nine of the 24 countries in Africa where they used to occur, largely as a result of habitat changes and hunting pressures.

Orang-utans – faces in the forest

These large, but shy and gentle apes are now found only in tropical forests on the islands of Sumatra and Borneo, off the southeastern coast of Asia. They tend to live alone, each one occupying its own territory. The female's range is relatively small, averaging about 2km^2 (0.75 miles^2), while a male occupies an area of 8km^2 (3 miles^2), in which a number of females may be found. To announce his presence - and to deter incursions by other males - the established male will roar loudly at intervals, and this noise carries through the jungle. Orang-utans spend most of their lives in the trees, swinging or climbing from branch to branch. They feed almost exclusively on fruit and vegetation, but may also eat invertebrates and even birds' eggs. Each animal knows its territory well, and heads unerringly for trees that are likely to be in fruit, remaining in the vicinity until the food is exhausted. After mating, it will be nine months before the baby orang-utan is born, weighing about 1.8kg(4lb). It has a far less dense covering of the distinctive reddish-brown hair than its mother and grows slowly. Young orang-utans are not weaned until they are about three years old, and remain close to their mother for a similar period. They can live for over 30 years, but as it takes so long to rear their young, females have a very low reproductive rate, producing as few as four offspring during their lifetime.

Communication signals are vital for survival and need to be learnt. These include the noisy, repeated breaking of twigs to indicate danger.

The agility of the orang-utan is clearly illustrated here, but it takes time for youngsters to gain sufficient confidence and strength to move like this. Their mother teaches them to climb trees.

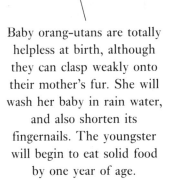

Baby orang-utans are totally helpless at birth, although they can clasp weakly onto their mother's fur. She will wash her baby in rain water, and also shorten its fingernails. The youngster will begin to eat solid food by one year of age.

It appears that orang-utans once ranged over a much wider area, being found on mainland Asia. They grew as large as today's gorillas.

❏ Orang-utans can easily become obese unless they have adequate exercise. A normal healthy male weighs about 91kg(200lb), but an individual in captive surroundings can weigh as much as 204kg(450lb).

❏ 'Orang-utan' is the Malay word for 'man of the woods'.

❏ Native to just two islands, these great apes are particularly vulnerable to the effects of habitat changes. Forest sanctuaries have been set up in an attempt to safeguard their future.

❏ The great apes were not thought to have any particular artistic talent, but an orang-utan called Djakarta Jim managed to confound critics in the art world. Following his win in an art competition held in the state of Kansas, USA during 1971, where he exhibited under the name of 'D. James Orang', he became an international star before his true identity was revealed. Orang's paintings enabled Topeka Zoo in Kansas to purchase a female companion for him, but after this, he showed no further interest in his artistic endeavours!

❏ Young orang-utans have pinkish faces, which darken as they become older. Males have swellings on the sides of their faces, called flanges. Orang-utans from Sumatra have less prominent flanges than those from Borneo.

Gorillas – gentle giants

An adult male west African lowland gorilla. Gorillas can use their hands in a similar way to man.

The sheer strength of these muscular primates is seen here. Gorillas balance on their knuckles, keeping their hind feet flat. They can adopt a semi-vertical stance.

When stories of gorillas first reached Europe in the 1600s, these great apes were invariably portrayed as aggressive giants that regularly killed people. The image has tended to persist in human imagination, and films such as King Kong have only served to reinforce this mistaken belief. Largely as a result of human persecution, relatively few gorillas are left alive, and they face an uncertain future. Gorillas are found in certain forested areas of western and central Africa, where they live in groups of up to 30 individuals, occupying a territory of 30km^2(12 miles^2). They spend most of their time on the ground, although youngsters sometimes climb trees in search of fruits and foliage. They have evolved a sophisticated system of communication; their vocabulary may consist of at least 22 distinct calls. Dominant males are recognizable by their silver backs, while younger males have black hair on this part of the body. When they mature, they may choose to leave and join another group, and as gorillas share their territory with other groups, this is not difficult. When a young male establishes his own group, he may try to steal one or more females from another male and this can lead to conflict, with young gorillas being killed. Normally, adults are tolerant of young gorillas in their group and there is a strong bond between mother and baby; parenthood is largely the responsibility of the female. She carries her baby until it is at least eight weeks old, by which time it will start to crawl. Young gorillas begin walking at about six months, but are not fully independent until three years old.

Gorillas live a fairly structured life, eating in the morning and resting until afternoon. The youngsters often use this time as an opportunity for playing with other members of the troop.

The silver back indicates that this gorilla is a dominant male, at least 12 years old. There may be a second, younger silverback who will take over as leader.

A 9-year-old male lowland gorilla playing with a 2-year-old baby. Young gorillas are curious by nature.

Gorillas usually sleep in nests made from branches and other vegetation. Youngsters sleep close to females.

❏ The mountain gorilla is the largest of all living primates, but rarely exceeds 1.8m(6ft).

❏ Gorillas used to be hunted· for their hands and heads, which were made into grotesque tourist souvenirs. Today, thankfully, this sickening trade is effectively outlawed. Small groups of tourists are now encouraged to visit gorillas under the supervision of experienced guides. This stimulates the protection of gorillas by local people, who benefit from the money spent by the visitors.

❏ Gorillas often resent being stared at by people at close quarters. In gorilla society, this is perceived as a challenge.

❏ There appears to be only one documented case of a person being killed by a gorilla. The incident took place in 1910 in Uganda, and vividly confirms the enormous potential strength of these great apes. A member of the Boringo tribe disturbed a gorilla family and was attacked by the large male of the group. His body was later found with its head and an arm torn off. Fred Mersfield, a hunter, had a close escape when he tried to shoot a gorilla. He was left with a badly gored thigh.

❏ Few predators will attack gorillas, but leopards are known to kill them. It appears that they strike while the gorillas are asleep at night and catch them unawares.

Toothless mammals — strange specialists

Smell is a vital sense for the giant anteater to locate food.

There may be little obvious similarity between anteaters, sloths and armadillos, but they are grouped together as edentates. This literally means 'toothless', but is really inaccurate, because both armadillos and sloths do possess rudimentary teeth. These are in the form of molars, although they lack the hard covering of enamel that is usually associated with mammalian teeth. The ancestors of this diverse group originated in North America and then spread southwards. As the sea level rose, the two landmasses became separated and the two populations of the group continued to evolve in isolation. Today, edentates vary in size from the lesser fairy armadillo, weighing just 80gm(3oz) up to the giant anteater, which can be as heavy as 40kg (88lb). Whereas most anteaters feed in the open primarily on ants and termites, sloths search for food in the tropical rainforests. They spend virtually their entire lives clambering slowly around the branches, clinging on with their 10cm(4in)-long claws. Sloths have virtually lost their ability to walk, since their front limbs are now much longer than their hind legs, and they are forced to drag themselves along on the ground as a result. Armadillos can be readily distinguished from all other mammals by their body armour. This is made up of bone encased in horn, and covers the entire back and sides of the body, as well as the tail and the top of the head. The name 'armadillo' originates from the Spanish and literally means 'little armoured one'.

The body covering of the armadillo is not totally rigid. It has some small folds of skin where hair may grow.

The southern tamandua, or collared anteater, is less than half the size of the giant anteater. This tree-dwelling species has a prehensile tail which helps it to climb.

The brown-throated, three-toed sloth's long claws and flexible grip enable it to move easily through the trees.

Sloths have a very flexible neck made up of nine vertebrae - more than in any other mammal.

When probing in a nest, the giant anteater can flick its 60cm(24in) tongue in and out of its small mouth about 150 times per minute.

❏ The three-toed sloth, found in the rainforests of Central and South America, has the distinction of being the world's slowest-moving land mammal. On average it travels at a leisurely speed of just 0.11kph (0.068mph) and covers about 38m(125ft) in a day.

❏ The sloth's brown teeth grow throughout its life and have no covering of enamel. There are just five teeth in the upper jaw and four in the bottom. The stomach is equally specialized, being divided into various chambers where the diet of vegetation is broken down in stages.

❏ If attacked, the anteater (above) sits back on its long tail and strikes out with sharp 10cm(4in)-long claws. The powerful forelimbs can inflict a crushing blow at close range.

❏ Microscopic green algae colonize and grow on the hair of sloths, camouflaging these slow-moving creatures. Certain moths may also be found in the hair of sloths. They are agile and move rapidly through the dense strands of hair.

Rabbits, hares and pikas – fast breeders

Rabbits have a better sense of sight than hares, but generally, hearing is the most important sense for this group of mammals. All of them, including this black-tailed jack rabbit, face a wide range of potential predators.

Representatives of this group, known collectively as lagomorphs, are found throughout the world, from rocky upland areas to the Arctic, and from tropical forests to open grassland. Pikas, with their rounded ears, may appear to be closer to guinea pigs (which are rodents), but they share the characteristic features of the lagomorphs. The most obvious are the three pairs of incisor teeth in the upper jaw at the front of the mouth at birth. The outer pair are soon lost, but adult lagomorphs retain two pairs of incisor teeth throughout their lives, whereas rodents have just one pair. In addition, their testes are located in front of the penis, rather than behind it, as is usual in mammals other than marsupials. Lagomorphs also have an unusual digestive system. At night, they produce soft droppings, which they eat, and finally they produce round faecal pellets. By this process, known as refection, lagomorphs can benefit from vitamins produced by bacteria in the lower part of the digestive tract, where they cannot be absorbed. Hares can generally be distinguished from rabbits by their longer legs, although there is a more significant distinction in their lifestyles. Whereas rabbits usually live in communal burrows, hares have shallow scrapes, known as forms, where they rest and give birth to their young. These leverets are far more developed than baby rabbits (kits). Some pikas live in burrows, while others nest among rocks. Facing a wide range of predators, the lagomorphs' lifespan tends to be short and their reproductive rate is correspondingly high. European rabbits can have five litters in rapid succession, producing over 30 offspring. In favourable conditions, they may assume plague proportions and can prove very damaging in agricultural areas.

Pikas are very noisy animals and may be audible at any stage of the day. Their calls travel over a distance of some 100m (330ft) or more.

Long ears are a most distinctive feature of rabbits and hares. They are kept horizontal when the animal is resting, but will be held erect at the first hint of any potential danger.

During the summer, the North American pika collects flowers, mosses and other vegetation for its hay store. These piles of dried grasses are stored under a rock face or close to the burrow to sustain the pikas in winter when other foods are in short supply.

Rabbits can unleash a painful kick if handled carelessly. This thrust also provides a means of escaping predators, as they run back to the safety of the burrow.

Young rabbits are most likely to be seen out of their burrows feeding in the early morning. Five rabbits grazing on a pasture can eat as much in a day as a sheep.

Rats and mice – potential plague carriers

There is really no means of distinguishing between mice and rats, although mice tend to be smaller. Together, nearly 500 species of these rodents are known throughout the world, and few creatures have proved more adaptable. One reason for their success is their high reproductive rate; when food is plentiful, many species multiply very quickly. Fluctuations in population are probably best known in lemmings, but can also be observed in house mice. In parts of Australia, they can reach huge numbers when grain is readily available. Some rats, such as the naked mole rat, have evolved highly specialized lifestyles. As its name suggests, this rodent is hairless, apart from whiskers, and it is blind. Living in groups of up to 40 individuals, each colony reveals a degree of social organization similar to that found in bees. Only one female breeds and she is attended by the larger members of the group. The remaining mole rats are responsible for tunnelling and obtaining food. When large numbers of rodents are in contact with humans, the possibilities for the spread of disease increase. The black rat is the most notorious carrier of bubonic plague, while Lassa fever (a virus) is associated with the multi-mammate mouse in West Africa, and tularemia (a bacterial disease causing aches and fever), is often isolated from voles, notably in parts of Eastern Europe and Asia.

Rodents, such as this brown, or Norway, rat move inside in winter and destroy large quantities of stored grain.

The harvest mouse is only 5.7cm(2.25in) long, but has a 5cm(2in) prehensile tail. It supports the mouse as it climbs among grass and corn stalks, eating seeds, insects and berries.

The brown rat is found wherever man provides food and shelter. It is able to swim and can survive near canals, rivers and in sewers. The Australian water rat has waterproof fur and webbed hind feet.

The leaf-eared mouse is active during daylight hours in the Andes Mountains at 4,300m (14,100ft). It feeds on seeds and plants.

Rats and mice have a keen sense of smell that enables them to find food and establish territories.

The black rat is generally smaller than the brown rat. Black-and-white individuals occur in the wild.

These prolific rats have a pregnancy lasting 24 days. A female gives birth to about eight offspring and can have up to six litters a year.

Chinchillas and cavies – the lovable rodents

Both these rodent groups are found in the New World, and have been widely domesticated, although for different reasons. Chinchillas are found at high altitudes within the Andean region of South America. They have very dense, soft fur that provides insulation against the cold, but also led almost to their extinction. At one time, chinchilla fur coats were very fashionable, and since it takes the pelts of at least 150 animals to make a single coat, their numbers declined dramatically. During the 1920s, it was decided to farm chinchillas and the success of this scheme indirectly helped to protect the surviving wild population. A number of colour mutations have since been developed in captive stock, and although no longer widely kept for their fur, chinchillas have become very popular as pets. The cavy, or guinea pig, is also a familiar pet in many countries. For many centuries, these small rodents were kept as a source of food in their South American homeland, running around the homes of the native Indians. They were brought to Europe during the 1500s. Most other cavies are larger but similar in shape, with a rounded head and no tail. They are all vegetarian, feeding on plants, and live in colonies. The maras, from Central and South America, are more harelike in appearance and pair for life. All cavies have a relatively long gestation period that may last for up to 90 days. The youngsters are born as miniature adults, with their eyes open and fur on their bodies. They run around almost at once and start to eat food within a day of being born.

Capybaras have a big head, with powerful incisors backed up by molar teeth.

The Patagonian cavy, or mara. Females have four long nipples on the sides of the body, one pair close to the forelimbs, and the other on the abdomen.

Maras usually give birth to just two youngsters that may stay with their mother for up to nine months. They clean their faces with their front legs.

The height of these large rodents enables them to wade into water to graze on aquatic plants. They also feed on crops and are hunted for this reason and also for their meat.

Capybaras are less social than many rodents and usually live in groups of less than 20 individuals. These strong swimmers can remain well concealed in the water.

Capybaras normally, walk slowly, but if frightened may leap away at some speed. There are three toes on each hind foot, and four at the front. They terminate in nails, with signs of webbing between them.

The chinchilla's long ears are about 6cm(2in) tall and well-covered with fur to protect them from the cold of their native land.

The unique qualities of their fur led to the near extinction of these rodents. Remarkably, each hair follicle can yield as many as 80 separate hairs, thus creating a very dense coat.

The relatively long, bushy tail may be held erect or curled close to the body, as here.

Squirrels – alert and bushy tailed

These rodents are all relatively similar in appearance, with a long body and bushy tail. They often rest sitting on their hindquarters, but remain constantly alert to possible danger. Some squirrels, such as the grey, spend most of their time in the trees, running up and down vertical surfaces without difficulty. The flying squirrel has evolved a stage further, with membranes of skin linking the front and hind legs to each side of the body. By holding its legs out when it leaps, a flying squirrel can glide across to another tree, relying on its tail to provide direction. The giant flying squirrel is able to cover distances of 100m(330ft), although no squirrel is able to fly properly. Certain squirrels, such as the prairie dog, live on the ground. They are highly social by nature and live in groups known as coteries, consisting of a male and several females, together with their youngsters. Prairie dogs are a form of burrowing squirrel, living in colonies of 2,000 individuals or more. Squirrels feed on nuts and other plant matter, including bark, which they chisel off with their powerful incisor teeth. When food is scarce in winter, squirrels from temperate areas, such as woodchuck, may hibernate. Their body temperature may fall to just a few degrees above zero and they rely on their stores of body fat to nourish them. Some squirrels prepare larders of food; Siberian chipmunks amass huge amounts, keeping up to 6kg(13lb) of food in their burrows to eat after emerging from hibernation.

Young ground squirrels near the mouth of their burrow in the arid Kalahari region of Africa. They start breeding at one year. Up to three offspring form the normal litter.

These squirrels eat seeds, roots and insects. They can breed throughout the year, but all females in a colony tend to give birth at the same time.

Grey squirrels are native to North America, but have been introduced to the UK. They feed on items such as fir cones, but may strip bark, killing trees.

Flying squirrels vary the position of the tail to steer them in flight. They can cover 50m (167ft), landing safely with their sharp claws. Their large eyes enable them to see at night.

The bushy tail may acquire a white edging in summer. When the squirrel runs or leaps, it extends its tail out behind the body.

Flying squirrels are found only in forested areas.

❑ Squirrels can play an important part in the spread of trees, by carrying food up to 30m(100ft) from where they find it. They may bury seeds and nuts below ground, but a proportion of these will not be reclaimed and eventually germinate in the soil.

❑ Squirrels can fall from a considerable height without injuring themselves. A Mexican tree squirrel was seen to fall a distance of 180m (590ft) without suffering.

❑ Many of the squirrels that live in trees build special nests, called drays, out of twigs and other material. They remain here when the weather is bad in winter, occasionally venturing out to drink and feed. They may wrap their thick bushy tail around them for additional insulation when resting in cold weather.

❑ The shrew-faced ground squirrel is unusual in that it is largely insectivorous, searching for grubs on the ground. Other ground squirrels can become agricultural pests and may be persecuted.

Beavers – the dam builders

With their thick, waterproof coats, the two species of beaver, one found in found in North America and the other in Europe, are well adapted to living in or near the water. Their webbed feet help them to swim effectively and their scaly broad tail provides extra speed in the water, but can be something of a handicap on land. The so-called mountain beaver, found in the western part of the USA, is not a true beaver. Rather than construct a dam, it prefers to tunnel and it does not swim, nor does it live in colonies. The sharp incisor teeth, characteristic of rodents, enable beavers to fell even quite large saplings, and these form the foundations of the dam. A pool of water develops and the beavers construct their lodge in the centre, piling up branches and sticks and adding mud for extra insulation and to anchor the structure together. Over a period of several years, successive generations of beavers will work constantly to add to the dam and lodge, with the result that these can develop into sizeable constructions. The beavers are careful to enter the lodge via a subterranean tunnel below the water level, which conceals their presence. When they dive, special membranes cover their eyes and ears and if danger threatens, beavers can remain submerged for 15 minutes or so. Young beavers are born in the lodge and can swim virtually from birth, although they are unlikely to leave their safe haven until they are about six weeks old. Beavers remain together as a family group for two years, by which time the young are sufficiently skilled to build their own homes.

Beavers fell trees growing as close to the water as possible and will not venture more than about 200m(650ft) onto land. They are sometimes killed by falling trees. If the trunk is thick, the beavers take it in turns to gnaw through it and may eat the bark if it is palatable.

Out of its aquatic environment, the beaver is relatively clumsy. On land, it walks slowly on all fours, diving noisily back into the water if frightened. This warns other beavers in the area of impending danger, but normally beavers enter the water quietly.

The beaver's eyes and ears are relatively small and both are covered by a protective membrane when the animal is under water.

The beaver's lodge and dam. It is one of the few mammals to alter the landscape in the area where it decides to settle.

The dense fur consists of two layers: a thick, fine greyish underfur and longer, coarser guard hairs that give the coat a rather shiny appearance.

The virtually hairless, broadened tail is one of the beaver's most distinctive features. The five digits on each front foot have sharp claws for gripping trees and branches. Beavers can fell a small sapling in five minutes.

❑ Beavers have been heavily hunted for their fur in many parts of their range, and this has had a serious impact on their numbers, especially of the European beaver. Only a few populations remain.

❑ The destructive capabilities of beavers are enormous. They can alter an entire landscape within a short space of time - few creatures other than man are able to do this. A single pair of beavers is known to have felled 266 trees in a period of just 15 months. They used the timber to build three dams, each one about 15m(50ft) in length. They also constructed a lodge, estimated to be 28.3 cubic metres (1,000 cubic feet) in size. Having felled a tree at its base, it is then gnawed into smaller lengths that can be dragged to the dam site or into the water to form the lodge.

❑ The largest known dam ever constructed by a colony of beavers, over several successive generations, was located on the Jefferson River in Montana, USA. It measured 700m(2,300ft) in length and could be crossed by a rider on horseback. Regular dams are about 23m(75ft) long.

49

Whales – giants of the oceans

Few groups of mammals are better known than whales and yet, despite their widespread distribution throughout the world's oceans, they are rarely seen. Whales are adapted to spend more time submerged under water than any other mammals, and are able to dive to great depths. Sperm whales, for example, can dive down over 1,100m(3,600ft), remaining under water for as long as 90 minutes. However, being mammals, they must breathe oxygen and are eventually forced to return to the surface. Their bodies have adapted to reduce their oxygen requirement to a minimum; for example, their blood is able to absorb more oxygen than our own, and their heartbeat slows down significantly when they dive. The huge bulk of many whales helps them to conserve body heat, even in the freezing polar oceans, where baleen, or whalebone, whales congregate to feed on swarms of tiny planktonic animals. They also have stores of body fat that provide insulation. In some whales, the blubber can be as much as 50cm (20in) thick. Many whales may undertake long migrations and feed very little on such journeys, relying on their fat stores to sustain them. Young whales are born in the oceans, and although the females do not have conspicuous nipples, they suckle their young in the usual mammalian way. The calves are usually weaned by about seven months.

Humpbacks are quite slow swimmers. They have been heavily hunted and their numbers have fallen sharply in various parts of their range.

In the past, humpbacks were never encountered around Hawaii, but are often seen there now.

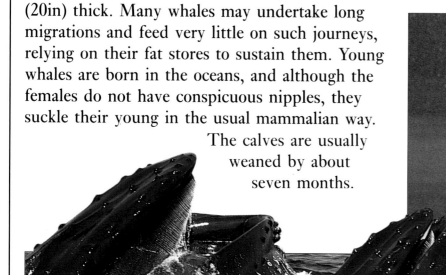

Humpback whales feed on krill and shoaling fish by lungeing upwards with their mouths open. Groups may cooperate in feeding.

Although weighing up to 30 tonnes (66,150lb), the humpback is surprisingly agile, and is quite often seen breaching.

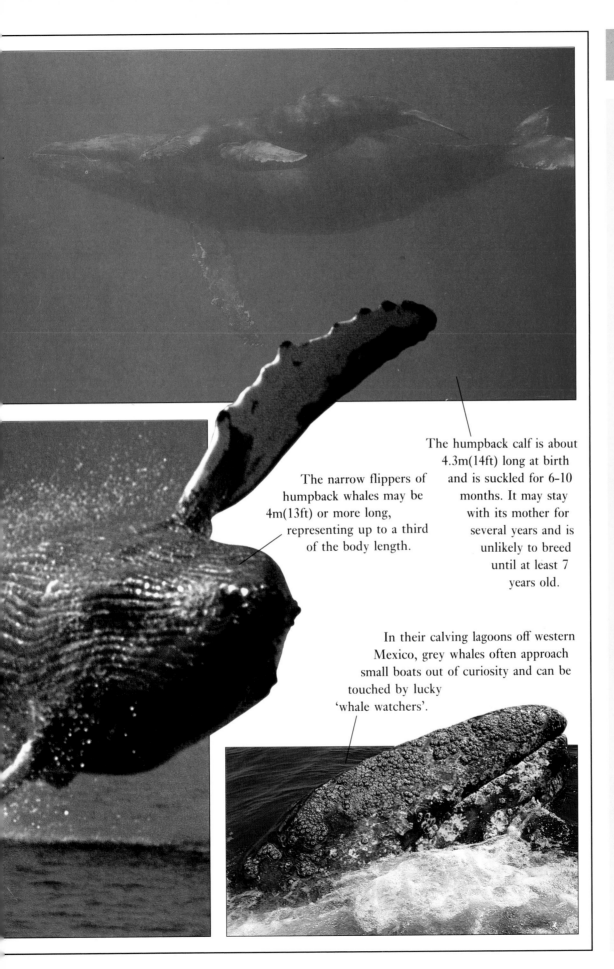

The narrow flippers of humpback whales may be 4m(13ft) or more long, representing up to a third of the body length.

The humpback calf is about 4.3m(14ft) long at birth and is suckled for 6-10 months. It may stay with its mother for several years and is unlikely to breed until at least 7 years old.

In their calving lagoons off western Mexico, grey whales often approach small boats out of curiosity and can be touched by lucky 'whale watchers'.

Dolphins and porpoises – sleek and playful

These smaller members of the whale clan are sometimes found in fresh water, as well as in the ocean. Four species of river dolphin live in the rivers of South America and Asia, but their numbers appear to be declining as a result of pollution of these waterways, coupled with intensive fishing. Freshwater dolphins are less intelligent than their marine relatives, and this is thought to be related to the fact that they lead a solitary existence, rather than living in groups. However, marine dolphins are known to hunt fish and other prey in a cooperative fashion, driving a school of fish into the shallows, for example, where it is easier to feed upon them. Dolphins communicate with each other by a range of sounds, varying from clicking calls up to high-pitched ultrasounds that are inaudible to our ears. In all, 32 species of dolphin and porpoise are known to live in the world's oceans, and within this group there are some surprises. The killer whale, for example, is classified as a dolphin rather than a whale, and is the largest member of the family, weighing up to 4.5 tonnes (9,920lb). This voracious predator sometimes ventures close to the shore, hunting fish, seals and penguins. It has sharp teeth and is able to seize and kill such prey without difficulty. In most members of the group, pregnancy averages about 11 months. The notable exception is Risso's dolphin, with a gestation period of up to 16 months. This species is also unusual in having a maximum of eight teeth in its lower jaw, whereas common dolphins have over 100 teeth.

A bottlenose dolphin breaks through the water surface in a playful gesture described as 'breaching'. Dolphins must surface regularly to breathe and the blowhole on the top of the head enables them to take in air without leaving the water.

Bottlenose dolphins can be found in oceans around the world. They are powerful swimmers, relying on their tail for thrust, and their sleek body shape to minimize water resistance. These dolphins feed almost exclusively on fish.

Spotted dolphins are quite acrobatic and have been seen cartwheeling and swimming upside down, as well as bow riding in front of boats. They have been heavily hunted off the coast of Japan and their numbers have fallen quite dramatically.

The dorsal fin may resemble that of a fish, but dolphins are undoubtedly mammals.

The bottlenose dolphin has a short 'beak', with up to 100 teeth in the jaws. They are often seen off the eastern coast of the USA.

Bottlenose dolphins usually inhabit coastal waters, living alone or in groups of up to 1,000 individuals.

FACT FILE

❏ Of all marine mammals, killer whales (above) are the fastest swimmers. They can move at up to 65kph(40mph).

❏ A school estimated at 100,000 migrating dolphins was observed in the Black Sea - the largest number of whales or dolphins seen together.

❏ Mammals are normally born head-first, but dolphins and whales are born tail-first to reduce the risk of drowning. The youngster does not start breathing until its head emerges from the birth canal; if it was born head-first and there was any delay in the birth process, its lungs might fill with water. As soon as the calf is born, its mother nudges it up to the surface so it can start to breathe.

❏ Dolphins, like whales, may run ashore and be stranded. The reason may be linked to the earth's magnetic field. Local variations caused by the geology of the area could result in the creatures becoming misdirected. Without help they are likely to die.

❏ Dolphins have been known to kill sharks that threaten a calf by ramming them.

Wolves – the ancestors of the domestic dog

Only two species of wolf still survive today. The red wolf is virtually extinct in the wild, although it used to roam widely across the southeastern corner of the United States, and the better-known grey wolf has undergone a similar contraction in its range.

The grey wolf has powerful jaws, capable of exerting a pressure equivalent to 15kg/cm² (33lb/0.15in²). They eat about 4kg(8.8lb) of meat in a day, more if very hungry, but rarely eat every day.

This species used to have the widest distribution of all land mammals, occurring across virtually the entire Northern Hemisphere, but a combination of hunting pressures and increasing urbanization, especially in western Europe, have led to the virtual extinction of the species. A few relic populations do survive, especially in Spain, while in North America, eastern Europe and Asia, wolves are still relatively numerous. They have been sighted at 5,791m(9,000ft) up in the Himalayas, higher than any other carnivore. Wolves live in packs of up to 20 individuals and each pack may establish a large territory that can extend over an area of 1,000km²(390 miles²). Scent marking signals their occupation, and fighting may take place if another group attempts to cross the territory. Within each pack there is a dominant pair, and often the female of this pair is the only one to breed. Other pack members assist in hunting and help to provide food for the resulting pups. A large pack can overcome a moose, which would constitute a dangerous challenge for a small number of wolves, but where smaller prey is available, the pack size itself is correspondingly reduced. In some areas, wolves have adapted to human incursions on their territory and scavenge after dark at rubbish dumps.

The number of wolves in an area is directly related to the availability of food. Pack size is also limited by the ability of the wolves to catch sufficient prey.

Coyotes are only found in North America. They live in pairs or small packs, frequently scavenging around human settlements.

The maned wolf found in South America lives alone and hunts mainly small mammals, birds and even snails. Despite its name, it is actually a fox. Wolves that live in the forests of North America are sometimes called timber wolves, but they are actually grey wolves.

The long-legged maned wolf can run very quickly through the grasslands, but it has been heavily hunted and few survive today.

Grey wolves howling. Communication is vital, as individuals often become separated from the pack.

After a two-month gestation, the female gives birth to up to 10 young in the den and the male brings them food.

When hunting, a wolf pack tends to target particular animals in a herd, aiming for young, weak or sick individuals that will put up little resistance.

❏ Wolves vary greatly in size throughout their wide range. The smallest wolves, weighing just 12kg(27lb), originate from the steppes of Asia, while the largest race is found in Alaska and may weigh as much as 80kg(177lb). The wide range of sizes in domestic dogs, which evolved from wolves, is not, therefore, entirely surprising. The domestication process probably began about 10,000 years ago.

❏ Wolves fail to obtain prey in as many as 90 percent of their attempts, and may go for days without food. Pups are particularly vulnerable to the effects of starvation and must travel perhaps 8km(5miles) a day, in order to keep up with the pack. Wolves do not usually attack people, and seek to avoid human contact. They do sometimes prey on farm stock and rabid wolves are potentially dangerous.

❏ Wolves howl loudly to keep in touch with each other and to warn off other packs. Their calls may be audible from a distance of 16km(10miles).

Foxes – crafty and adaptable

The cape fox is sometimes described as the bat-eared fox.

These are small foxes, even when adult, and their pale coloration helps them to merge easily into their background. They are mainly insectivorous, but also eat fruit and berries and sometimes hunt small animals, such as lizards and birds.

While the range of wolves has declined in the face of increasing urbanization, that of foxes has tended to expand. Today, populations of urban foxes are likely to be encountered in major city centres, perhaps even during daylight hours. The red fox now has the widest range of all mammals in the Northern Hemisphere, being absent only from central Greenland. Its distribution extends southwards as far as parts of North Africa and Central America. One reason for the enormous distribution of this species is its feeding habit. The red fox will feed on almost anything edible, and although it prefers birds and small mammals, it will consume large quantities of fruit if other foods are not available. Whereas wolves live in packs, foxes are solitary by nature, which makes them less conspicuous. Of the 21 species, a number are found in South America, including the crab-eating fox. Most are reddish brown or even blackish, but the Arctic fox, found in the far north, undergoes a seasonal change in coloration to help it blend into the landscape. When there is permanent snow cover on the ground it has a white coat, but dark hairs will regrow during the spring. In order to reduce heat loss from its body, the Arctic fox has evolved small ears and an especially dense coat to provide insulation. As a result, this species has been heavily hunted for its fur, both in its white and 'blue' forms. Between 1900 and 1920, foxes were farmed extensively for their fur in North America. One farm employing 400 workers sold millions of dollars worth of pelts to the fashion industry.

The red fox's long tail, or 'brush' often has darker markings. Melanistic (black) foxes are quite common in North America and the Baltic region.

The Arctic fox is highly adaptable in its feeding habits, catching rodents and birds, and scavenging off the kills of large animals, including polar bears. In winter, its feet are protected by dense hair.

Mating occurs during the first two months of the year and the cubs are born about 52 days later. The vixen gives birth in an underground den to an average of four cubs.

Both parents take part in rearing their young, but if the vixen is killed the male may rear them on his own. They start taking solid food from four weeks.

FACT FILE

❏ Red foxes have incredible stamina and are known to reach speeds of 48kph (30mph). They can also swim and can jump obstacles up to 2m(6.5.ft) high.

❏ In mainland Europe, the red fox is the main reservoir of rabies infection. In the past, attempts to eliminate red foxes have proved singularly unsuccessful, and now the emphasis has switched to vaccinating them, with the aid of special baits.

❏ The fennec fox (above) of northern Africa, is the smallest fox, weighing just 1kg(2.2lb). Its large sensitive ears detect the insects, rodents and birds on which it preys in the desert.

❏ There used to be a small and remarkably tame species of fox on the Falkland Islands, off the coast of South America. However, large numbers were killed for their pelts, and when settlers began raising sheep in the 1860s, the widespread use of poison finally eliminated the species, last sighted in 1876.

Bears – seekers of solitude

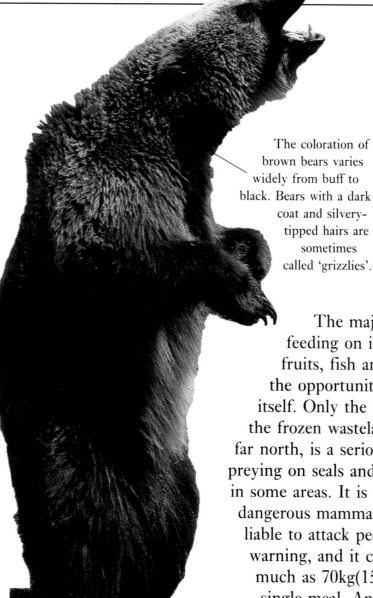

The coloration of brown bears varies widely from buff to black. Bears with a dark coat and silvery-tipped hairs are sometimes called 'grizzlies'.

Bears are the world's largest terrestrial carnivores, but their ancestors were little bigger than foxes. Today, the centre of their distribution is the Northern Hemisphere, but nowhere are they common. Bears live solitary lives, wandering over large areas in search of food.

The majority are omnivorous, feeding on insects, plants, fruits, fish and also meat, if the opportunity presents itself. Only the polar bear, in the frozen wastelands of the far north, is a serious hunter, preying on seals and even reindeer in some areas. It is one of the most dangerous mammals on the planet, liable to attack people without warning, and it can consume as much as 70kg(154lb) of food at a single meal. Apart from the polar bear, bears represent little direct danger to people and seek to avoid human contact.

Because they inhabit colder parts of the world, many bears retreat to caves where they pass the winter in a state of torpor. Here, females may give birth to up to four youngsters. The offspring are tiny, weighing as little as 200gm(7oz), and the warmth within the den helps to ensure their survival. By the following spring, the bears will have grown to about 10kg(22lb) and venture into the outside world for the first time with their mother. They remain with her until they are at least one year old, and she defends them ferociously from potential dangers, such as wolves.

Brown bears used to occur from North Africa across Europe and Asia and into North America. Hunting and urbanization have reduced their numbers.

Bears are opportunistic feeders. This brown bear is feeding on a salmon captured as it migrates upstream to its spawning grounds.

Playful encounters among cubs form useful lessons for adult life. They are immensely powerful.

Polar bears can remain submerged for two minutes or more, but rarely dive deeper than 2m(6.6ft). They can swim up to 95km(60 miles) paddling with their front paws.

Young bears mature quite quickly; females may breed at only four years old, but do not produce a second litter for another four years.

It is dangerous to approach the highly protective female bear with cubs. At an early age, the cubs are taught to climb trees to escape from predators. These can include roaming adult males that attack cubs and may kill their mother.

❏ The spectacled bear used to be widely distributed throughout northern South America, but is now found only in Ecuador and northern Peru. It has become the rarest of all bears, with a total population of less than 2,000 individuals.

❏ The Malayan sun bear (above) is the smallest species of bear, standing just 70cm (27in) high at the shoulder, and weighing only 27kg(60lb).

❏ The Kodiak bear, which lives on Kodiak and nearby islands in the Gulf of Alaska, can measure over 2.5m(8ft) long and weigh as much as 751kg (1,656lb). It is believed to be the largest of all bears, but recent reports from the USSR suggest that even bigger individuals may be found in the eastern part of that region.

❏ The sloth bear is adapted to feed on termites. It lacks the inner pair of incisor teeth at the front of its mouth and has no hair on its lips, so it can suck the termites into its mouth.

Giant pandas – adapted to live on bamboo

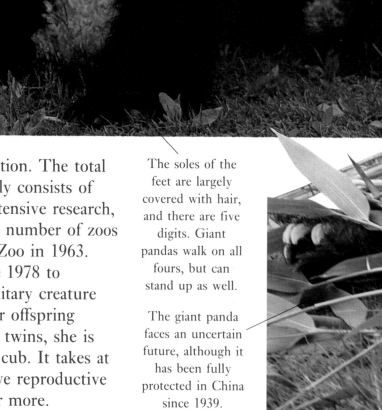

Although now considered to be a close relative of the bears, the giant panda is unique in a number of ways. Most obviously, perhaps, its coat is not a single colour and its front paws have evolved so that it can feed effectively on bamboo. This plant forms the basis of its diet and the giant panda can hold the bamboo very effectively with its enlarged wrist bones and gnaw at the shoots. It also eats insects and animals, such as bamboo rats. Unfortunately, its specialist feeding habits are a threat to its very existence, because stands of bamboo die back after flowering, thus depriving pandas of their food source. In the past, they would have moved on to a new locality, but clearance of areas of bamboo has made this increasingly difficult and in some cases pandas are faced with starvation. The total wild population of the giant panda probably consists of less than 500 individuals, but thanks to intensive research, cubs are starting to breed successfully in a number of zoos around the world, beginning with Peking Zoo in 1963. Artificial insemination has been used since 1978 to increase the numbers of this species. A solitary creature by nature, the giant panda female rears her offspring independently. Although she may produce twins, she is rarely successful at rearing more than one cub. It takes at least four years for young pandas to achieve reproductive maturity, but they may live for 20 years or more.

The soles of the feet are largely covered with hair, and there are five digits. Giant pandas walk on all fours, but can stand up as well.

The giant panda faces an uncertain future, although it has been fully protected in China since 1939.

The giant panda's head is enlarged by the muscles needed to chew the hard bamboo stems. The nose is not covered by fur.

Giant pandas feed for about 11 hours daily, sitting down to gnaw bamboo stems with their strong teeth.

The white areas of the panda's fur often have a yellowish tinge.

❏ The plight of the giant panda led to its adoption as the symbol of the World Wide Fund for Nature (formerly called the World Wildlife Fund). It has since become the best known of all the endangered species.

❏ For a long time, zoologists have argued whether the giant panda is a bear or a member of the raccoon family. The smaller red panda (above) is more closely associated with the latter group. It is found in a similar environment to the giant panda but generally occurs at higher altitudes and sleeps in trees during the day.

❏ Giant pandas are entirely covered with white fur at birth, and only develop their adult pattern of coloration at about one month old. They develop surprisingly slowly; for example, their eyes do not open until they are nearly two months old and they may not start to feed on their own for the first time until they are nearly four months old. Their mother will continue to suckle them for a further two months.

Weasels – cunning killers

Despite their relatively small size, weasels and their relatives, including stoats and polecats, are formidable hunters. They generally prove highly adaptable in their feeding habits, taking small mammals, worms, fish and birds, although some species are more specialist hunters. The black-footed ferret, for example, found on the western prairies in the USA, hunts only prairie dogs. However, its numbers have declined as its prey has been eliminated by human intervention and it is now considered to be endangered. These mammals may undergo a striking change in their coat coloration during the winter, which helps to conceal them from potential prey. For example, in summer the stoat is brown with lighter underparts. As it starts to moult, white areas extend from the bib over the rest of the body and it takes on a pure white coloration, except for the very tip of its tail, which remains dark. At this stage it appears to be a totally different animal; a stoat in its winter coat is often described as ermine and its white fur was once highly prized. Weasels are traditionally hunted by gamekeepers for killing young pheasants and similar game, but they are surprisingly prolific creatures. Females may breed up to three times a year, giving birth to their young in a snug nest. They teach their offspring how to hunt, continuing to do so even after weaning has taken place. If food supplies are plentiful, the young weasels in turn can begin breeding at just four months of age.

The common weasel has a vast distribution, extending across virtually the whole of Europe, with the notable exceptions of Ireland and the southern part of the Iberian Peninsula. It occurs southwards into Africa and eastwards right across Asia and into Japan.

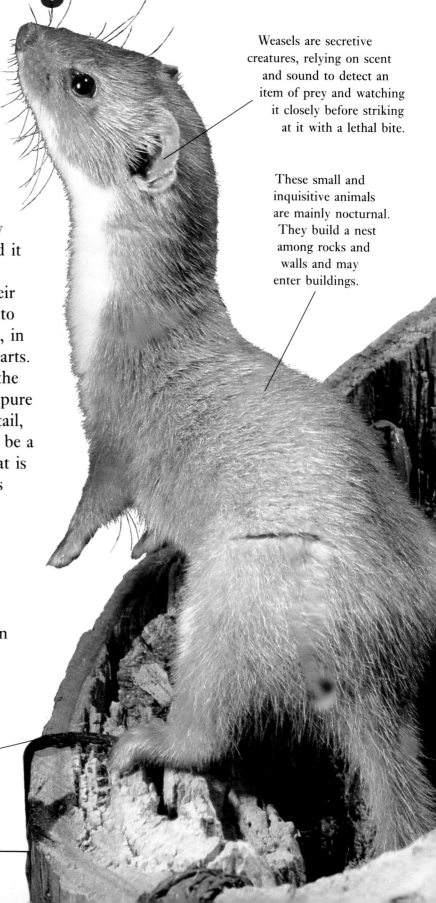

Weasels are secretive creatures, relying on scent and sound to detect an item of prey and watching it closely before striking at it with a lethal bite.

These small and inquisitive animals are mainly nocturnal. They build a nest among rocks and walls and may enter buildings.

A long-tailed weasel in its white winter coat. This species is widely distributed in the New World, from Canada south to Bolivia.

The marten's tail helps to provide balance. It can climb with ease.

Martens are found mainly in forested areas, spending much of their time in trees.

Keen eyesight enables martens to leap among the branches.

❏ The European polecat (above) is thought to be the ancestor of the domestic ferret. Its domestication may have begun as early as AD 20, because ferrets were regarded as invaluable for killing rodents and rabbits. Today's ferrets are noticeably different in colour from polecats; they are generally pale yellow.

❏ Weasels were introduced to New Zealand on several occasions, beginning in 1867, as a means of controlling the rabbits that were plaguing the islands. Unfortunately, and perhaps not unexpectedly with hindsight, these adaptable predators have since inflicted enormous damage on much of New Zealand's unique fauna. The rare flightless kakapo parrot that breeds on the ground is very vulnerable.

❏ The least weasel is the smallest carnivore in the world. It measures just 18cm(7in) long, including its tail, and weighs about 35gm(1.2oz). Nevertheless, it is a ferocious predator, feeding primarily on rodents. Least weasels occur in many parts of the world; those from the New World are the smallest of them all.

Mongooses – nimble carnivores

These carnivores are found mainly in Africa and on the neighbouring island of Madagascar, although seven of the 31 species occur in southern Asia. They are nimble, quick hunters and although some do kill poisonous snakes, mongooses generally take a much wider range of prey. The crab-eating mongoose, for example, feeds mainly on crustaceans and, along with the marsh mongoose, may catch frogs. Other mongooses feed on insects and rodents. They have proved intelligent and adaptable creatures. If it finds a duck's nest, for example, the marsh mongoose has learnt that the best way to crack the eggs is to throw them against rocks. Most mongooses live on the ground, but some, such as the ringtailed mongoose from Madagascar, hunt in the trees. Meerkats are social by nature and live in family groups in underground burrows, but most mongooses live alone and hunt at night. Under favourable conditions, mongooses can prove quite prolific, with females producing up to eight youngsters at a time. In the social species, maternal duties may be shared between several females, but the female mongoose generally rears her youngsters alone. Mongooses have been introduced to various islands, notably in the Caribbean, to control the rodents that plagued the sugar cane fields, but they also preyed upon native species, and are now themselves considered to be pests.

Yellow mongooses looking out for danger close to their burrow. They usually take over dens excavated by other animals, such as springhares, and may share the burrow alongside them. They may range considerable distances in search of food.

Mongooses are agile creatures, able to walk on all fours yet also capable of standing up on their hindlimbs to view their surroundings.

A pack of banded mongooses, occupying an abandoned termite mound. They occur in dry areas of Africa, darting down into their burrow if danger threatens.

Mongooses search for food during the day, making the best use of their keen eyesight and good sense of smell.

Banded mongooses may hunt in packs of up to 50 animals, although more commonly in pairs.

The dwarf mongoose is an African species, well-equipped to wrestle with prey using its 36 teeth. These mongooses are active during the day and often hunt in groups.

❏ In the dwarf mongooses, which live in groups, there is a clearly defined social structure in the community. The young animals are responsible for acting as guards, alerting the colony to potential danger, and have a shrill call for this purpose. Females are dominant and a strict hierarchy is established. The dominant female and her mate are the only members out of a typical colony of a dozen individuals that will breed. All other members of the colony help to care for the young and they, as well as the dominant pair, have priority for food. Mature members of the group remain in the colony, even though they may not breed. Once the dominant female dies, the colony is likely to break up, with some females forming new groups elsewhere.

❏ Scent marking is important as a means of communication for all mongooses, whether they live alone or in colonies. Anal sacs attached to glands mean that scent is deposited along with faeces within the mongoose's territory.

❏ Unlike most species, mongooses in Madagascar may burrow and are also agile tree-climbers. They may catch birds, and steal both eggs and chicks from nests.

❏ Mongooses communicate by means of high-pitched sounds and also by body posture. For example, stamping the hind feet is a sign of aggression.

Tigers – stalkers in the night

The largest member of the cat family, the tiger, is solitary by nature and hunts alone. It prefers large prey and may sometimes attack humans. Once a tiger has killed a person, it becomes a very dangerous creature, as it is more likely to strike again. Under normal circumstances, wild pig and deer – and occasionally young elephants – form the basis of the tiger's diet. The tiger is confined to areas of forest and mangrove in parts of Asia, and its numbers have decreased dramatically during recent years. Each animal covers a large territory, which can extend up to 100km² (39 miles²) in the case of a male. His territory may overlap that of three or four females, but there is little contact between them unless they are mating and then a pair may stay together for several days. The female gives birth in a den and up to four cubs form the typical litter, each weighing about 1kg (2.2lb) at birth. Their stripes are paler than those of adult animals. At about two months they begin to take solid food, and soon after they start accompanying their mother on hunting excursions. Tigers do not make a kill every day, but a large carcass provides food for several days; the female hides it carefully in the undergrowth, returning to the spot to feed with her offspring. Cubs may remain with the tigress for up to two-and-a-half years before leaving to establish their own territories.

The Indian tiger often preys on domestic cattle and buffalo. It needs an average of 3 tonnes (6,075lb) of meat annually, eating up to 50kg (110lb) in a single meal after a kill.

A tiger must learn to hunt in order to survive, and it is quite common for a tigress to seize prey and hold it so that her cubs can learn how to kill efficiently.

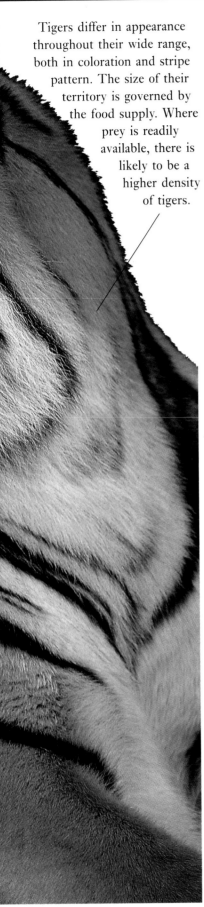

Tigers differ in appearance throughout their wide range, both in coloration and stripe pattern. The size of their territory is governed by the food supply. Where prey is readily available, there is likely to be a higher density of tigers.

White tigers sometimes occur in the wild, especially in the Rewa district of India. The Maharajah started breeding these striking creatures in 1951.

Tiger cubs are unlikely to hunt on their own before they are a year old. They generally start by taking small prey.

Lions – predators of the plains

Today, lions are confined almost exclusively to Africa, although they used to range across southern parts of Europe and into Asia. They face few enemies in the wild, but have suffered heavily from human persecution. In India there is a tiny surviving population, protected as far as possible in the Gir Forest Sanctuary. Lions are the most social of all wild cats, living in groups called 'prides' made up of as many as 15 females and one or more males, which can be easily distinguished by the longer mane of hair around the neck. In spite of their ferocious appearance, male lions are not closely involved in hunting prey. This is essentially the task of the females, who work together to take large prey, such as zebras and wildebeest. They try to encircle the chosen animal as far as possible, before launching into a rapid gallop to catch and drag the unfortunate beast down to the ground. At this stage, the males are likely to feed on the kill, often before the lionesses. Male lions do have a relatively hazardous existence, however, as they are constantly being challenged by others. Although there is a strong dominance hierarchy within the pride, a male from outside may attempt to move in and take over, displacing the established male. Alternatively, there may be a challenge from another male within the group, although succesion under these circumstances is generally less traumatic. Even a strong male is unlikely to maintain his position of dominance for more than three years. Displaced males then adopt a solitary lifestyle. Lions appear to be the longest-lived of the big cats, with a possible lifespan of nearly 30 years.

The roar of the male lion can carry over a distance of 8km(5 miles). No other cat roars in this way.

After giving birth in a secluded locality, a lioness will not remain with her cubs constantly. If hunting proves difficult, she may be away for two days at a time. These two-week-old cubs will join the pride in about one month.

Lionesses hunt together and this behaviour is instinctive, but efficient killing is a critical lesson that offspring must be taught.

Male lions are unique in possessing a mane of thick fur around the neck. Its function is to help protect this vulnerable region of the body when the animals are fighting. The coloration of the mane varies from blond to black, depending both on the individual creature and the population concerned.

❏ When a new male takes over a pride, he is likely to kill any existing young cubs. The lionesses are then able to mate sooner and he can pass on his genes more quickly.

❏ Lions, tigers and leopards are the only big cats known with certainty to be potential man-eaters. In lions, it seems that the whole pride develops a taste for human flesh. The most notorious case of recent times was a pride that lived in the vicinity of Lake Nyasa in Tanzania. Between 1932 and 1947, when they were finally eliminated, they slaughtered an estimated 1,500 people. Injury can also drive individual lions to attack people, because they are less alert than the lion's traditional quarry. A lion that killed eight people, also in Tanzania, was found to have only three legs when it was finally shot in 1977.

The pride may walk up to 10km (6 miles) every night, especially when prey is in short supply. Lions rely heavily on the cover provided by grass to conceal their presence from prey.

❏ On average, lions spend about 20 hours a day resting. When they do hunt, they are likely to make a successful kill in only two attempts out of ten.

Leopards – stealthy hunters

Extending across most of Africa, mainly south of the Sahara, and eastwards as far as parts of China, leopards have the largest distribution of any wild cat. Yet they are rarely seen, preferring to hunt at night and remaining hidden in grassland or other vegetative cover during the day. Leopards generally prey on smaller animals, such as rabbits, which are easy to catch, but adult leopards may sometimes seize and kill large antelope. If they choose to pursue game, they can run at speeds up to 60kph(37mph) over short distances, and may swim if necessary. Melanistic leopards are sometimes seen, particularly in Asia. They are born alongside normal-coloured individuals in a litter, but are instantly recognizable by their black coloration. For a period, they were called black panthers, until it was realized that they were simply a form of the leopard. Indeed, they retain the same pattern of markings, visible as slightly darker areas on their black coats. However, the snow leopard is a distinct species, usually found at relatively high altitudes in the Himalayas and other parts of Asia, where it roams over vast areas in search of prey, eating virtually anything from small rodents and birds to deer and wild boar. The clouded leopard occurs further south in Asia, extending to Sumatra and Borneo. Little is known about its habits, but it appears to spend most of its time in the trees, pursuing monkeys and birds, which it stuns with a blow from its broad paws.

The clouded leopard is found in forested areas, and has short legs, enabling it to climb easily. Unlike most other large cats, leopards often climb trees to rest and even leap down onto unsuspecting prey passing beneath them.

Snow leopards often have dens among the rocks to which they return at regular intervals. These highly agile climbers have also been seen in the trees - in vultures' nests.

The leopard has disappeared from many parts of its enormous range, but has proved a very adaptable cat, requiring just a supply of suitable prey and water to prosper. It appears to have no specific habitat requirements, being essentially an opportunistic and efficient hunter.

In some areas, leopards may develop specific feeding preferences. This is what can make them dangerous to humans: once a leopard has attacked a person, it is likely to strike again.

The markings of leopards vary noticeably throughout their range and relate to the animal's habitat, ensuring that it has good camouflage. These cats hunt alone, not in groups.

FACT FILE

❑ Leopards have long been hunted for their skins, but in areas where they are well protected, such as the various national parks in Africa, these shy cats have become more visible during the daytime.

❑ It is thought that the melanistic form of the leopard is more numerous in Asia because leopards occur in forested areas there, rather than on open plains, and their coloration enables them to blend in well against this darker background.

❑ Leopards have proved more adaptable than tigers, probably because they feed on a much wider variety of smaller prey, including dung beetles, fish and even dogs.

❑ In favourable areas, there can be one leopard in each square kilometre (0.4 mile²), although an average density of one per 25km² (10 mile²) is about average.

❑ When hunting, a leopard can cover 25km(15miles), and to escape danger, they have been known to cover as much as 75km(45miles) in one explosive burst of speed.

❑ Leopards often drag their prey up into a tree, where it will be out of reach of scavenging carnivores such as hyenas. A leopard has even been known to pull a young giraffe weighing 90kg(203lb) over a branch some 3.6m(12ft) off the ground.

Cheetahs – the athletic cats of Africa

The jaws of the cheetah are less powerful than those of larger cats.

The fastest member of the cat family, the cheetah, has amazing acceleration over short distances, although it is not adapted to pursue prey for more than a minute or so. Should the cheetah fail to reach its target by this stage, it gives up the chase. Stealth is thus an equally important part of the cheetah's hunting strategy and it moves as close as possible to its prey before revealing its position. It prefers small prey, such as hares, gazelles and bustards. The cheetah's pace helps it to avoid direct competition with other predators, such as lions, and it also tends to be active during the hottest part of the day. But other creatures, such as vultures, may move in and drive the cheetah off its hard-earned catch. Female cheetahs are at a serious disadvantage when they are pregnant, because the weight of their cubs inevitably slows them down. The task of rearing the cubs also falls to the female alone, and weaning takes three months. After this, the young may remain with their mother for well over a year, but mortality among the cubs is high. Out of the average litter of three, only one is likely to survive to reach maturity. The range of the cheetah has contracted during recent years, and today their last remaining stronghold is in Africa. Increasing urbanization of their habitat is the major problem, although hunting for their skins has also been a contributory factor in their decline.

Cheetahs tend to breed during the wet season. When it is dry, game is concentrated around the remaining waterholes and females find it easier to make a kill, but predators of young cheetahs, such as jackals, are also more of a threat at this time.

The cheetah is capable of attaining a maximum speed of at least 90kph(56mph) over short distances.

Keeping cheetahs for hunting began in Africa, over 5,000 years ago. With their slim, lithe bodies, they are well adapted for sprinting, and are unique among cats in not being able to retract their claws once adult.

The cheetah must remain constantly on the lookout for danger.

When they are born, cheetah cubs weigh no more than 300gm(11oz) and measure a mere 30cm(12in). As they grow, they are taken to the site of the kill, rather than having food brought to them at their den. This probably makes them less vulnerable to predators.

New World cats – shy and secretive

A margay in a hollow log. It hunts among trees, climbing down head first and dropping onto prey from above.

Pumas have the widest distribution of the wild cats found in the Americas, ranging from Canada southwards as far as Argentina, but they are shy and rarely seen. The same applies to the smaller wild cat species found in this part of the world. As recently as January 1986, a new type of cat, previously unrecognized by zoologists, was discovered in Mexico, where it had remained largely hidden. Missionaries and other travellers had reported sightings, but none had been taken seriously until this individual was finally shot. The onza, as it is now known, is similar to the puma in appearance, but has longer legs and is reputed to be more aggressive. Its distribution appears confined to the northwest of Mexico, and is centred on the states of Sinaloa and Sonora. Also present in Central America, and extending as far south as Patagonia, is the jaguar. It is grouped with the big cats, and is very similar in its habits to the leopard. It hunts a wide variety of game, from monkeys and sloths in the trees, to deer and wild pigs ambushed on the ground. Jaguars have also been known to lie by a river or stream and grab fish that are drawn to the surface. They can swim well and even catch freshwater turtles and caiman. Eight species of small cat can be found in parts of South America. They are distinguished from their larger relatives by being unable to roar and also by wrapping the tail around themselves when they lie down, rather than extending it behind them.

The ocelot is an agile tree-climber and may even sleep off the ground. It can also swim well if necessary.

A puma at rest. These are normally very secretive animals but highly adaptable, being found in a wide range of habitats, where the climate can be extremely variable. They are also known as cougars and mountain lions.

It has been suggested that jaguars flick their tail in the water to attract fish and then scoop up their catch with their paws. They are heavily built animals; males weigh about 150kg(330lb).

The jaguar is usually found close to water and takes a wide variety of prey, including fish and mammals, such as peccaries - tusked, piglike animals - that come there to drink.

Seals – streamlined mammals of the sea

Seals are one of the few mammal groups to have adapted to an aquatic lifestyle. Nearly all species live in the oceans, but there is a population of freshwater seals in Lake Baikal in the Soviet Union, about 1,600km(1,000 miles) from the sea. The seals' round shape and powerful flippers allow them to power through the water at speed, hunting fish and other aquatic creatures, but they still return to land to give birth to their pups. Large groups, often made up of thousands of individuals, gather together at breeding time and male seals, known as bulls, battle ferociously to establish harems. Mating occurs soon after the cows have given birth, and then the seals disperse back to the ocean. This tends to be an annual cycle, and in a number of species the development of the fertilized egg is slowed down at first. It does not implant into the wall of the uterus immediately, but remains in a state of suspended animation for some months. In this way, the period of pregnancy is effectively extended until the same time the following year.

The seal's hind limbs are modified to extend behind the body. They act rather like a tail, enabling the seal to swim effectively. The muscles in this part of the body also aid swimming ability.

As with the hind limbs, the bones of the forelimbs are greatly shortened. Seals may use these limbs to move around on land. All seals have a covering of fur and a layer of fat beneath the skin to provide insulation.

Seals are carnivores. Their molar teeth have sharp edges and are modified to help them grab food under water. When submerged, seals close their nostrils.

Fur seals on a South
African beach.
The young are
valued for
their pelts.

The walrus' long tusks
are modified canine teeth.
They grow throughout
the animal's life.

Two elephant seals fighting.
The strongest bulls
acquire the largest
harems, with up
to 40 cows.

Walruses live in family
groups consisting of a bull
with several cows and
their calves, as well as
larger groups of young
males. Molluscs form the
major part of their diet
and they dig these up
with their tusks.

❏ Californian sea lions can
swim at speeds of 40kph
(25mph), making them the
fastest members of the seal
family in water. The crabeater
seal, found in the Antarctic,
moves quickest on land - at a
speed of 19kph(12mph).

❏ The Weddell seal can dive
to depths of 305m(1,000ft). It
survives the water pressure at
this depth by collapsing its
lungs and then reinflating them
as it returns to the surface.
Seals may stay submerged for
as long as an hour, but come
up to breathe at air holes that
they keep open in the ice.

❏ Out of about 34 species of
seal, the largest is probably
the southern elephant seal
(pictured above). Bulls can
reach 4.9m(16ft) long and
weigh as much as 2,268kg
(5,000lb), although there have
been reports of walruses
reaching a similar size.

Elephants – trunked giants

The Asian elephant is smaller than its African relative, with much smaller ears and generally less prominent tusks.

There are two separate populations of elephants, and while much attention has been focused on the plight of the African species, it is the Asian elephant that is rarer. Its total population probably does not exceed 50,000 individuals. It is possible to distinguish between the two species at a glance, as the African elephant has much larger ears and is generally bigger overall, averaging about 3.3m(10.8ft) in height. Asian elephants are about 30cm(12in) smaller. Their habits are remarkably similar; they spend much of the day feeding and, being vegetarians, they must consume a vast amount of food – up to 150kg(330lb) daily – to meet their energy requirements. Their characteristic trunk acts rather like a hand, enabling them to pull down foliage, which they break off and put in their mouths. Water is sucked up in a similar fashion, and squirted into the mouth. Elephants may drink over 80 litres(17.6 gallons) each day, and rarely stray far from water. They are social animals and live in herds presided over by a cow who is usually the oldest member of the group. She knows the territory well, and can lead the herd to food and water, even when supplies are short. Younger elephants learn from her example. Bulls only join a herd during the breeding period. Pregnancy lasts a long time in elephants, averaging around 22 months, and a single youngster is usually born. It suckles directly from the mother's mammary glands, which are located on the chest between the front legs, using its mouth rather than its trunk. A calf may need 11.4 litres(2.5 gallons) of milk each day, and will depend on its mother for ten months or so. It remains in her company for several years at least, although most young bull elephants leave when they reach 14 years old.

Elephants will travel across considerable distances in search of food, crossing rivers if necessary.

❏ The elephant's trunk, the result of a fusion of the nostrils and upper lip, is operated by about 150,000 muscle fibres, which give it great dexterity. One cow was able to crack open peanuts and blow away the debris before picking up the tiny nut kernels, using her trunk for each of these tasks.

❏ The elephant's tusks are specialized incisor teeth, growing out from the upper jaw. They grow throughout life. The legendary African elephant 'Ahmed' (shown above) that lived in the Marsabit National Reserve in Kenya, had superb tusks measuring 285cm(112in) and 297cm(117in) respectively. Each one weighed 67kg (148lb). The longest recorded African elephant tusks measured 326.4cm(128.5in) and the heaviest weighed 102.7kg(226.5lb).

❏ Elephants are vital to their environment in many ways; their dung helps to provide fertilizer for the soil, and their paths can serve as firebreaks.

Locked in combat, two young bulls wrestle with each other. Such playful sparring is normal and rarely results in injury.

The skin of an elephant can be up to 4cm(1.5in) thick, but is very sensitive. Adults have little hair on the body, except around the eyes and tail, but the skin is covered in sweat glands, even between the toenails.

Elephants visit waterholes not only to drink, but also to cool off. They often use their trunks as shower hoses. Bathing keeps the skin in good condition.

Manatees and dugongs – mythical mermaids?

The teeth of adult manatees consist only of molars. As one is lost, the others move forward in the jaw.

Strange as it may seem, sea cows, or sirenians, are believed to share a common ancestry with elephants. Four species survive, and all graze on aquatic plants. While the dugong occurs in the Indo-Pacific Ocean, ranging from East Africa to Vanuatu, manatees inhabit rivers and estuaries on opposite sides of the Atlantic Ocean. It is thought that they crossed to Africa from South America when the continents were closer together than they are today. Unfortunately, these giants now face a number of threats to their survival. They have traditionally been hunted for their meat, but now pollution is damaging their feeding grounds. In parts of Florida, powerboats inflict serious, if not fatal injuries with their propellers. Sirenians are normally long-lived, with few natural predators, and their reproductive rate is correspondingly low. They are unlikely to breed until they are over five years old, and a single calf is born after a pregnancy of about 12 months. Manatees and dugongs are devoted mothers and nurse their young for about 18 months, although they start to eat on their own soon after they are born. The head and breasts of the female sirenian appearing above the waves are thought to be the basis for sailors' tales of mermaids. As mammals, they must come to the water surface to breathe, but otherwise, sirenians are totally aquatic.

Manatees consume about 30kg(66lb) of aquatic plants daily.

The forelimbs are modified into flippers. Although all sea cows have five fingers, the nails are often missing.

Manatees have a unique skeletal structure, being the only mammals with six vertebrae in the neck. The neck is not clearly defined, emphasizing their cylindrical outline.

The manatee swims with its forelegs and rounded tail. It has virtually lost its hind limbs, and is quite incapable of walking on land.

All manatees have a covering of hair before birth, but this is later lost.

Manatees in the Crystal River, Florida. If the water becomes cold, they can move towards the Blue Spring, where hot springs keep water temperatures above 21°C(70°F).

FACT FILE

❑ The biggest sirenian recorded during recent years was an American manatee caught in about 1910, in the sea off the state of Texas, USA. It measured 4.65m (15.25ft) long. Such an animal would probably weigh at least 907kg(2,000lb). In contrast, the Amazonian manatee, the smallest species, reaches a maximum length of about 2.5m(8.25ft), and tips the scales at just 140kg(309lb).

❑ At one time, a much bigger sirenian could be found, grazing on seaweed in shallow water off the coast of Bering Island in the North Pacific. Named after the captain who discovered it, when his ship was wrecked on the island in 1741, Steller's sea cow grew to nearly 9m(30ft) long, and may have weighed 7,893kg (17,400lb). Its total population probably did not exceed 2,000 individuals and after news of its discovery leaked out, many hundreds were killed for meat by visiting ships. The others were probably driven away to less suitable areas. It is generally accepted that this species had become extinct by 1768, just 27 years later, but there is evidence to suggest that a few individuals survived at least until 1854. In July 1962, the crew of a Russian whaler observed six similar creatures feeding on seaweed in a nearby lagoon in the Gulf of Anadyr. The possibility that other populations of sea cows might survive even today cannot be discounted.

Zebras – Africa's striped horses

Three different types of zebra are found in Africa and can be distinguished quite easily by their markings and the areas in which they occur. The commonest form is the plains, or Burchell's, zebra that lives in groups of several mares accompanied by a stallion. In contrast, Grevy's zebra from the northeastern part of the continent is found in loose groupings with no permanent social order. Males cover large areas – up to 10.25km^2(4 miles^2) – and do not stay in the company of a particular number of females. As their name suggests, mountain zebras are found at higher altitudes, in parts of southern Africa. They have evolved softer hooves that cushion them against the dry, rocky terrain. In all cases, when stallions decide to pursue females, they may fight each other, driving off rivals by kicking and biting. It is not unusual to see zebras in the company of other herbivores, including antelopes. This may offer them some protection against lions that prefer to pursue the antelope. Zebras do not run very fast and are vulnerable to attack. For this reason, young foals are born almost fully developed and are on their feet only hours after being born.

Adult zebras in the Ngorongoro Crater, Tanzania, live in family groups throughout their lives. These have a clear social ranking, with certain dominant mares and stallions.

Female zebras join other groups at maturity. Males remain in bachelor groups.

Older members of the zebra herd defend their young against predators by lashing out with their hooves.

❏ Zebras often associate with ostriches and wildebeest. It has been suggested that the acute eyesight of the birds, the hearing of the zebra and the sense of smell of the wildebeest provides a triple defence system, alerting all species to possible danger at the earliest opportunity.

❏ A horselike zebra called the quagga once lived in South Africa. It was brownish with contrasting white stripes on its head and neck. Very pale, indistinct stripes continued over the rest of its body. Early settlers kept quaggas among their herds of cattle to defend them from lions and they proved to be alert guards and aggressive if cornered. Unfortunately, quaggas also provided a plentiful supply of food and hides for the Boers as they settled in this area. Hunting began in earnest in the 1840s, and the last known wild quagga was killed during 1878. The only surviving member of the species died in Amsterdam Zoo in 1883.

❏ The name 'quagga' came from the unusual alarm calls of these animals. For a period, they were fashionable in London for pulling carriages.

❏ The nearest relative of the quagga was a form of Burchell's zebra found in the same part of Africa. This suffered a similar fate. It was already rare by 1850, and the last survivor was kept at London Zoo until 1910.

Body patterning is consistent between individuals of the same species. The depth of the dark markings is another useful identifying feature. This is a Burchell's zebra.

Grevy's zebra is the largest species, standing up to 1.6m(5.25ft) tall at the shoulder. Its stripes are very close together and in foals the mane extends right along the back.

Before fighting, the zebras face each another and one rears up to intimidate its opponent.

Females give birth to a single foal after a pregnancy lasting about a year. The mother remains very close to her foal, but it will be a few days before the young zebra recognizes her.

Tapirs – among the first big mammals

These browsing creatures may look like pigs, but they are most closely related to the rhinoceroses. Tapirs are an ancient group, whose ancestors evolved over 20 million years ago and they appear to have altered little in appearance since then. Four species still survive, with three of these being found in parts of Central and South America. The Malayan tapir, in contrast, inhabits the jungles of Burma and Thailand, extending across Southeast Asia as far as the island of Sumatra. It is believed that tapirs existed in the days before today's continents were formed, and when the landmasses divided, so they drifted along with them. Tapirs are mainly nocturnal in their feeding habits, using their sensitive noses to locate suitable plants and grasses. They tend to live on their own, often preferring to stay close to water - even retreating into it if danger threatens and diving out of sight beneath the surface for several minutes.

This movable extension of the nose and upper lip is a typical feature of tapirs.

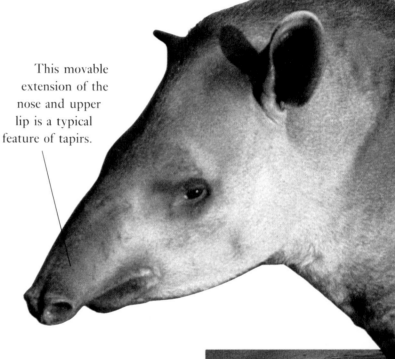

A six-week-old mountain tapir, born after a gestation period of 14 months. This is the smallest surviving form and weighs up to 250kg(550lb).

Females can breed throughout the year, and when they meet up with a potential partner, the pair circle each other, squealing quite loudly. After mating, they go their separate ways, and the young tapir may stay with its mother until it is nearly nine months old. At first, the young of all species have a dark coat broken by pale stripes and spots, which provide good camouflage within their jungle home. By the age of eight weeks, however, their appearance is beginning to change and within six months, the coloration of the young tapir will resemble that of an adult.

The Malayan tapir is the largest species and the only one surviving in the Old World. Its stocky shape enables it to push through the forest vegetation. Tapir skins are valued as a source of leather.

The ancestors of today's tapirs reached South America from the north about one million years ago. Their line died out in Europe at about the same time. This is an adult Brazilian tapir.

❑ Bathing (above) stimulates digestive activity and tapirs often enter water after feeding.

❑ The mountain tapir, found in the Andean Mountains up to altitudes of 4,500m(14,750ft) has a dense woolly coat to keep it warm. Other species have just a thin covering of hair. In the other two New World species, there is an area of dense bristles on the back of the neck that provides some protection against the bite of jaguars, which may leap down on top of a passing tapir and inflict a fatal wound.

❑ Tapirs depend primarily on smell rather than on sight, as they move through the forest. Their small eyes are located deep in the skull, so they are less likely to be injured by the dense vegetation.

❑ Under normal conditions, tapirs walk only on three toes. The fourth toe on each front foot is positioned slightly higher on the side of the feet than the others, and touches the ground only when the foot has sunk into soft terrain.

Rhinoceroses – fearsome horned herbivores

Two species of rhinoceros live in Africa, in relatively open country, whereas two of the three Asiatic species inhabit areas of rainforest. The Indian rhinoceros is the exception, frequenting grassland. Although it has a prominent horn on its nose, this species tends to attack with its sharp incisor teeth, rather than charging like its African relatives. In spite of their fearsome appearance, all rhinoceroses are vegetarian. The white rhino is adapted for grazing, with wide lips to pull at the grass, but its black relative browses on shoots and taller plants, looping its upper lip around them to pull off leaves. The structure of the rhinoceros' horn differs from that of other mammals because it lacks any bone at its centre. Instead, the horn is built up of layers of keratin, the tough protein substance from which hair is made. Rhino horn has spelt disaster for these huge herbivores. It has been favoured in oriental medicine as a means of providing potency, while in the Yemen, rhino horn daggers are a traditional symbol of wealth. Other factors, notably extensive deforestation in Asia, have also contributed to a drastic decline in wild populations of both the Javan and Sumatran rhinoceroses. Large island species such as these are especially vulnerable to the effects of habitat change, and in spite of protective measures, their futures appear very bleak.

Female white rhinos with calves often live in small groups. Should danger threaten, they form a circle to protect their offspring.

White rhinos are more social than black ones, but the young calf may be killed by a bull wanting to mate with its mother. Soon after birth, the horn, derived from hair, is relatively inconspicuous.

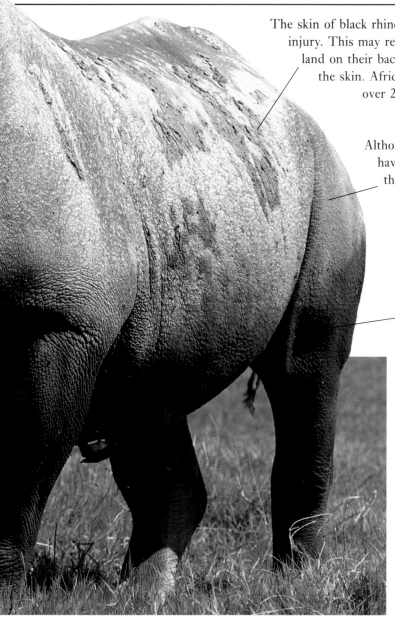

The skin of black rhinoceroses often shows signs of injury. This may result from oxpecker birds that land on their backs and pull out parasites from the skin. African rhinoceroses can be host to over 20 different species of tick.

Although herbivorous, rhinoceroses have few serious predators other than people. Occasionally, lions may attack a young calf, but adult rhinos generally ignore them, showing no signs of fear when they encounter a pride.

Charging rhinos can run at 40kph(25mph) over short distances. They have attacked passing vehicles.

An Indian rhinoceros and calf wallow in a waterhole, which helps to keep their skin in good condition. They may also graze on aquatic plants. These rhinos prove powerful swimmers, in spite of their bulk. At birth, the young calf probably weighed around 65kg(143lb), whereas adult males may weigh 2,000kg(4,410lb) or so.

FACT FILE

❑ The distinction between white and black rhinoceroses is not as clear as their names suggest, as they are virtually identical in coloration. The confusion arose because the first 'white' rhinos seen were quite light in colour, simply because they had been rolling on chalky soil, and acquired a whitish coating. The two species differ quite widely in temperament, however; white rhinos are far more docile than their black relatives.

❑ Rhinoceroses used to occur over a much wider area of the world. The woolly rhino, for example, lived in Europe during the last Ice Age, about 15,000 years ago. An extinct member of the group named *Indricotherium* is believed to have measured up to 5.5m (18ft) at the shoulder, and probably weighed a huge 20 tonnes (more than 40,000lb).

❑ It is estimated that there are probably less than 60 Javan rhinos alive today. Rhino populations generally have plummeted during recent decades. Studies suggest that the black rhino has fallen in numbers from about 60,000 in 1970 down to just 3,500 only 20 years later. Rhinos reproduce slowly, and if more than 10 percent of them die or are killed each year, their numbers will fall. However, the trend can be reversed. There are now more than 4,000 white rhinos in South Africa's Umfolozi Reserve; in 1900, there were just 50.

Hippopotamuses – forced to live in water

Hippos have four webbed toes that they can spread slightly to help them swim.

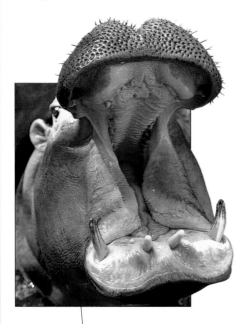

The large canine teeth in the lower jaw can be used to inflict deep wounds.

Although it is sometimes known as the water horse, the hippopotamus is most closely related to the pigs. These bulky mammals are found close to water across a broad band of Africa, south of the Sahara. They have peculiarly thin skin, with glands that produce a red secretion resembling blood, which protects them from sunburn. It may also have useful antibiotic-like properties, since hippos rarely develop signs of skin infection, even after serious injuries, such as may be inflicted during conflict between individuals. The tusklike canine teeth can be used in combat, when males battle over an area of territory. Hippos are forced to spend most of the day submerged in water, but at night they clamber onto land to feed on vegetation. This lifestyle prevents a rapid loss of fluid from the skin, which could lead to severe dehydration. Hippos consume about 40kg(88lb) of plant matter each day, and in some areas over-grazing has proved a problem. The animals may cover nearly 3km(1.8 miles) overland to their feeding grounds, travelling along particular paths, which they mark with dung. Mating takes place during the dry season, so that the young hippos are born after the rains, when vegetation is most plentiful. After a gestation period of about 34 weeks, each cow usually produces a single calf, either on land or in a shallow stretch of water away from the main herd. She suckles it for at least eight months, and the youngster may live for over 40 years.

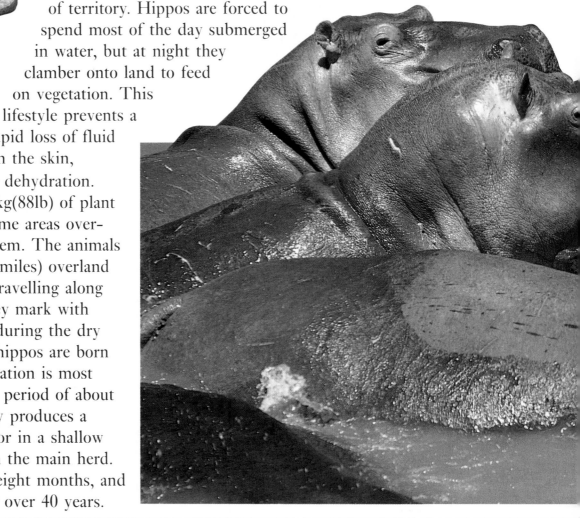

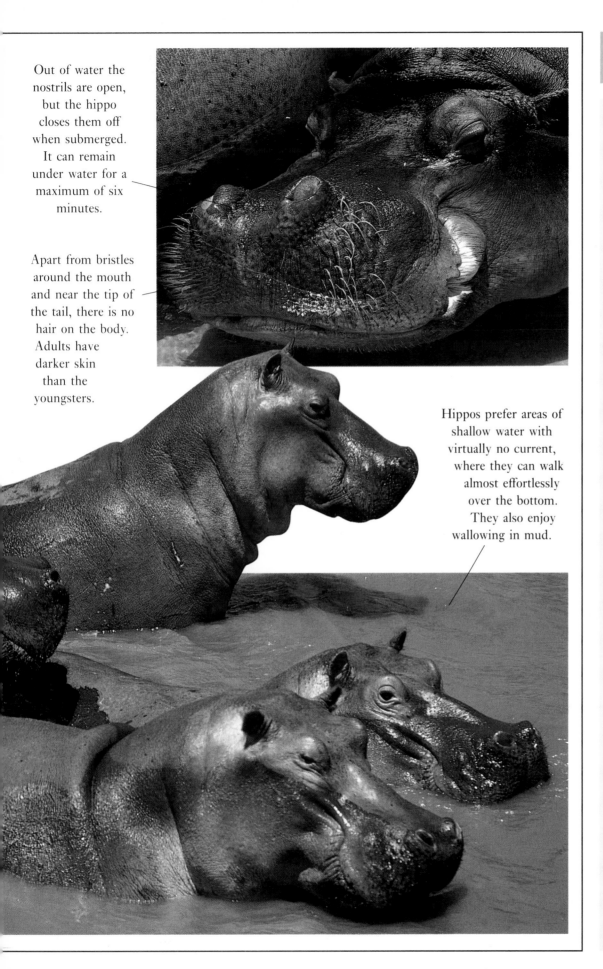

Out of water the nostrils are open, but the hippo closes them off when submerged. It can remain under water for a maximum of six minutes.

Apart from bristles around the mouth and near the tip of the tail, there is no hair on the body. Adults have darker skin than the youngsters.

Hippos prefer areas of shallow water with virtually no current, where they can walk almost effortlessly over the bottom. They also enjoy wallowing in mud.

❏ A number of creatures may be found on the hippopotamus body. Terrapins sometimes bask on the hippos' backs, while birds such as cattle egrets may also rest there, waiting quietly to grab passing fish from the water. A small fish belonging to the carp family often grazes on the algae that grows on the hippo's skin as a result of its long submersion in water.

❏ When the world's weather was warmer, hippopotamuses used to be found as far north as the UK. Individual forms also established themselves on a number of the islands in the Mediterranean, but did not attain the same sizes as their African relatives. They were eliminated by human hunting pressure at least 8,000 years ago. Today, the only other surviving hippo species is the pygmy hippopotamus (above) with a distribution centred on the forests of Liberia. It tends to be more terrestrial and smaller - about 1.75m(5.75ft) long and little more than 275kg(607lb) in weight. In contrast, the largest male hippopotamus can weigh as much as 3,200kg(7,072lb).

Vicuna are probably the original form of domesticated alpaca.

A female vicuna with her offspring. Vicuna are the smallest of the South American camelids.

Camels and llamas – sharp-toothed herbivores

Camelids, as these animals are collectively known, originated about 45 million years ago on the continent of North America. Although they have become extinct here, their descendants can still be found in western South America, where the llamas began to be domesticated more than 5,000 years ago. In the Old World, native people have also kept camels. The Arabian camel, or dromedary, has one hump, whereas the bactrian camel found in Asia has two. In the wild, camelids live in groups of one male and several females. They have a reputation for being rather unruly, and camels in particular are often bad tempered. Pregnancy lasts about a year and the single youngster is able to walk almost from birth. Camelids have also been introduced to other parts of the world as beasts of burden. The early explorers of Australia's vast interior found that Arabian camels proved adaptable to desert conditions, and a wild population of about 25,000 individuals is now established there. Camels were taken to the United States for military use. During the Civil War, the Confederate Army liberated a number of captured Arabian camels that bred in the state of Arkansas, until finally rounded up in the mid-1870s. The llamoids in South America have also been prized for centuries for their wool. Incas captured herds of vicuna on a regular basis for shearing, and alpaca wool is still in great demand today.

A bactrian camel has two humps. If the camel is dehydrated or hungry, the humps begin to sag.

As beasts of burden, camels can carry loads of up to 270kg (595lb). There are an estimated 15 million domesticated camels worldwide, a clear indication of their importance.

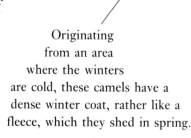

Originating from an area where the winters are cold, these camels have a dense winter coat, rather like a fleece, which they shed in spring.

A llama mare with her one-hour-old foal. The mother gives birth in a standing position and the single offspring is able to walk within about 30 minutes. Youngsters leave the herd at about one year old.

❑ Camels (shown above) are able to survive the effects of dehydration, as their kidneys produce a very concentrated urine, thus minimizing water loss from the body.

❑ Guanacos do not appear to drink, but obtain the water they need from their food.

❑ Vicuna, guanacos and llamas that live at altitudes of up to 5,486m(18,000ft) have undergone physiological changes to ensure survival. At such altitudes, the air is thin and its oxygen content reduced. To compensate, the haemoglobin in the red blood cells that carry oxygen around the body combines more effectively with the oxygen. Also, there are relatively more red blood cells, so that an increased volume of oxygen can be absorbed. The blood is thicker than normal and the heart muscle is more powerful so it can pump it effectively.

❑ Only a tiny handful of wild dromedaries - probably less than 500 - survive in their native area of southwestern Mongolia and the northwest of China. Here, they are considered endangered.

Deer – handsomely endowed for battle

The characteristic most closely associated with this group of ruminants is the presence of antlers on the heads of male deer. Antlers vary greatly in shape, from the broad antlers of moose, with a possible span of 2m(6.5ft) from tip to tip, through the branched antlers of reindeer to the simple spikes on the head of the pudu. Water deer also have antlers, and in reindeer, which occur further north in the Arctic than any other deer, both sexes - not just males - have antlers. This development is linked to the fight for survival. Antlers convey dominance within the herd and because female reindeer retain their antlers longer than males, they can exert a territorial advantage and obtain the best grazing sites for themselves and their offspring when food is scarce in winter. During the mating season, often known as the 'rut', stags use their antlers to battle for females. The antlers, which are made up of bone, are then shed and regrow the following year. In this way, young stags can develop progressively larger antlers as they mature, and exert greater dominance within their group. Not all deer associate in herds. For example, moose - the largest of the 39 species - measuring up to 2.3m(7.5ft) at the shoulder, live solitary lives; females do not seek out males until they are ready to mate.

The antlers may weigh as much as 25kg(55lb) and can have as many as 12 points.

A Rocky Mountain elk, also known under the traditional name of wapiti. When rutting, elk utter a call not unlike a yodel.

Mating takes place in autumn and the single youngster is born about nine months later. Rearing it is the responsibility of the female and she continues to suckle the youngster for several months.

The antlers are covered in a furry skin called velvet. In autumn, the deer rub their antlers against hard obstacles to remove the velvet.

A barasingha fawn suckling. These deer live in open country in northern India and often feed in swampland reedbeds.

A newborn white-tailed deer fawn. The mother licks it to remove any scent and it remains hidden as she grazes.

Two caribou, or reindeer stags, locked in combat. Each male may establish a harem of up to 15 females. The young are born in May and June and can walk within half-an-hour of birth.

Giraffe and okapi – the odd couple

Standing up to 5.8m(19ft) in height, the familiar giraffe is the tallest living animal in the world today. The okapi, measuring just 1.8m(6ft) high, is less well known, and there appears to be little obvious similarity between the two species, but the characteristic swellings on their heads, resembling horns, provide conclusive evidence of the link between them. Giraffes live in loose herds on the plains of Africa and evolved their height in order to graze on foliage that was out of reach of other terrestrial mammals. The okapi is also able to forage easily within its rainforest environment, where its rather unusual colour pattern helps to conceal its presence. The horns are normally larger in male animals, and are sometimes used in clashes between giraffes battling for females. In most cases, however, disputes are simply settled by neck-wrestling, with the giraffes entwining their long necks until one withdraws from the combat. A male giraffe will mate with females in his territory. Pregnancy lasts about 15 months, and then the female giraffe withdraws to a traditional calving area, where she gives birth to a single offspring.

Giraffes can see over a wider area than any other animal, thanks to their height. The normal seven vertebrae in the neck are greatly elongated.

The giraffe has a massive heart weighing 11kg(24lb) to pump blood up to the brain.

Giraffes can leap over a 2m (6.6ft) fence by holding the neck backwards and landing with the front feet first.

If cornered, giraffes can lash out strongly with their feet.

Giraffes are totally unable to swim, and avoid crossing deep stretches of water. They may look ungainly on their long legs, but are quite capable of running at speeds in excess of 50kph(31mph).

The okapi feeds on plants, using its strong tongue rather like a hand to curl round the leaves and pull them off the branches. It may also gnaw at trees burnt in lightning strikes to obtain charcoal.

The coloration and unusual striped pattern of the okapi helps to provide it with incredible camouflage in its forest environment. They may be totally invisible from a distance of 2.5m(8ft).

❏ The okapi (above), from northern Zaire, only became known to western scientists in 1900. At first, it was believed to be a relative of the horse; only later was its relationship with the giraffe confirmed.

❏ The pattern of markings on a giraffe is as unique as that of our own fingerprints.

❏ Female giraffes give birth while standing, so the newborn inevitably falls some 2m(6.6ft) to the ground. It instinctively manages to turn during this brief period to avoid falling on its head, and injuries are rare. It can stand after 30 minutes.

❏ Giraffes can safely eat plants with sharp thorns, because they produce large amounts of saliva that prevents the food sticking in the mouth or throat and because the roof of the mouth is toughened. Each animal may eat as much as 66kg (145lb) of food daily. Being so tall, they can reach vegetation that is out of reach to most other animals, but are forced to bend and splay their forelegs in order to drink.

Antelopes – adaptable relatives of cattle

Zoologists recognize a number of distinct groups of antelope. These include the nimble gazelles and their relatives, often described as dwarf antelopes. Although small, females tend to be bigger than their mates and their young probably stand a better chance of surviving because they can be born at a correspondingly larger size. In many of these species, individuals form a strong pair bond, and scent marking, via special scent glands, as well as with urine and dung, is important in maintaining their territories. Antelope species are at their most numerous in Africa, where the grasslands are home to the larger forms. Wildebeest associate in huge herds, thundering across the plains on their annual migration during the dry season, when grazing becomes sparse. Both sexes have horns. Hunting pressures have led to the decline of a number of antelope species, including the Arabian oryx and the scimitar oryx, but successful captive-breeding programmes have saved the former species from extinction. In contrast to these larger antelopes, the duikers are a shy and secretive group that inhabit the forests of Africa. Only one species, the common duiker, is found in more open country. They usually associate in pairs, with females producing a single calf. Both partners often wander widely throughout their territory of up to 4 hectares (10 acres), and they may not stay in close contact with each other. Duikers are also unusual because as well as eating vegetation of all kinds, they also consume rodents, insects and carrion.

Within the saiga's bulbous nose is a chamber lined with a mucous membrane that warms the air and filters out fine dust particles.

Sable antelopes occur in wooded parts of Africa, remaining close to drinking water. Groups of females and young are overseen by a single male who battles rivals.

Each of the horns of the male greater kudu can attain a total length of 1.2m(4ft). Their twisted shape enables these antelopes to wrestle each other without causing great injury. The contest becomes a test of strength, with the weaker individual retreating.

Large ears indicate keen hearing. If frightened, a herd runs a short distance and pauses, thus becoming an easy hunting target.

❏ The pronghorn antelope, found in the grassland and desert areas of the western USA is the fastest animal in the New World, sustaining its pace for longer than any other species. Herds can travel at about 72kph(45mph) for distances of at least 1.6km (1 mile). At their usual speed of 56kph(35mph), they can easily cover 6.4km (4 miles) without lessening their pace.

❏ Antelopes form the largest recorded herds of mammals ever seen. During the 19th century, when food became scarce in Africa, there were vast movements of springbok, as animals moved in search of fresh grazing. In 1849, one of these so-called 'trekbokkes' through Beaufort West in Cape Province reportedly lasted for three whole days. The last event of this type took place during July 1896, when a herd of an estimated 10 million springboks was observed close to the Orange River, stretching back about 222km (138 miles). Many animals starved and the wholesale destruction of springbok herds meant that such events were not to be repeated.

SUPERFACTS

The largest mammal

The blue whale is the largest known mammal in the world. At the end of the feeding season - in polar waters during the summer - a female blue whale can reach a weight of more than 200 tonnes (441,000lb). The longest blue whale on record is also a female - measuring 31m(101.7ft) from the tip of the jaws to the trailing edge of the enormous tail flukes. These figures are the exceptions rather than the rule; on average, blue whales weigh about 100-120 tonnes(220,500-264,600lb), with males usually measuring 25m(82ft) long and females 26.2m(85.9ft) long. Even at the 'standard' weight, a blue whale is equivalent to about 25 average-sized elephants - the largest land animal in the world.

Small but perfectly formed

Among the smallest of mammals, the spiny mouse is unusual among rodents in giving birth to young that are relatively well advanced. They are born with their eyes open, for example, a condition not seen in most rodents. To achieve this, the gestation period can be almost twice as long as in other small mice, at 36-40 days instead of the more usual 20-30 days. The common name of this mouse comes from the area of stiff, spiny hairs along the back.

The fast-food platypus

The platypus has a prodigious appetite. The first one kept at the Bronx Zoo in New York managed to eat 540 earthworms, 200 mealworms, 30 shrimps, 2 eggs and 2 frogs in the course of a single day, with its own body weight being just 1.5kg(3.3lb). As a gesture of affection, the male chews at the female's tail.

A sizable predator

The largest lion was 3.4m(11ft) long, excluding the tail. It was shot in Angola in 1973. Adult males normally reach 2m(6.6ft).

Blowing off steam

When a blue whale surfaces to breathe through its blowhole, exhaled air is released from the lungs under great pressure and may be visible as a plume of water vapour 9m(30ft) in height, the tallest blow of all the whales. A blue whale may breathe out and then inhale 200 litres (44 gallons) of air in just two seconds, which is equivalent to some 90 percent of the lungs' volume. Whales display a high ability to extract oxygen from the blood and then store it in their muscles.

Australian giants

Until about 10,000 years ago, there were giant forms of many of the marsupials seen in Australia today, including kangaroos and the koala. They are thought to have died out as the climate of Australia became progressively drier.

The original aqualung

The water opossum, found in parts of Central and South America, is one of the strangest of all marsupials. During the day it lives in a hollow in a river bank, emerging at night to catch aquatic creatures, such as crayfish and, occasionally, fish. The female water opossum can produce as many as seven youngsters at a time and at first she carries them in her pouch. This does not prevent her from swimming, because there is a sphincter muscle that closes off the entrance to the pouch when she is under water, making the interior watertight. The youngsters are able to continue breathing using the air trapped inside the pouch just like an aqualung.

Drag-racing mammals

As the fastest four-legged animal, the cheetah has astonishing acceleration, being able to reach a speed of 70kph(43mph) in just two seconds from a standing start, on its way to a top speed of 90kph(56mph) over a short distance. The cheetah must reach its prey within the first 400m(about 1,312ft), otherwise it is in danger of overheating and suffering brain damage. Such is the power in the hind limbs of a jack rabbit that it may briefly reach speeds of 72kph (45mph), leaping distances of 6m(20ft) at a single bound.

Bright monkeys of the north

Japanese macaques are found further north than any other monkey, frequently encountering snow in parts of their range. They are highly intelligent and social creatures, their behaviour giving rise to the legend of the three monkeys - 'see no evil, hear no evil, speak no evil'. Their adaptability is shown by a group of Japanese macaques that over a period of ten years learned to wash potatoes covered in sand given to them by scientists.

Island rarities

The rarest of all insectivores is probably Fontoynont's hedgehog tenrec, found on the island of Madagascar, off the southwest coast of Africa. Only one specimen has ever been recorded. Another island creature, the Sumatran hare, is equally rare; only 20 have been seen.

Headlong rush

The first account of the suicidal behaviour of Norwegian lemmings was recorded in 1532. Normally, the numbers of these rodents are kept in check by their many predators, which range from birds such as buzzards to weasels. Yet on occasion when environmental conditions are favourable, these rodents may continue breeding through the summer and into the winter, building up to very large numbers. If unchecked, these reach a point where the stress within the group becomes to severe that the colony is badly affected as a result. They then head off in large groups, almost unaffected by the terrain around them. They may swim rivers or cross glaciers at this time. Eventually, a high proportion of the lemmings will have died from stress or exhaustion, but there is no truth in the tale that they march onwards until they reach the sea, plunging over the cliffs to commit mass suicide.

Smells good

The human nose has 5 million 'smell' receptors but bloodhounds have 200 million on an olfactory membrane 50 times the size.

SUPERFACTS

Not all marsupials are Australian

The Virginia opossum is one of the species of marsupial found well away from Australia - the usual home of these pouched mammals. It occurs further north than any other marsupial and now ranges across the USA border into Canada.

Moles with stars in their nose

The starnosed mole of North America has the most bizarre nose of all mammals. The fleshy tentacles increase the sensitivity of the nose to touch, a vital sense for these creatures as they scurry almost totally blind along their subterranean tunnels in search of earthworms and beetles.

The devils of Tasmania

Not all marsupials are herbivores, as illustrated by the Tasmanian Devil. Confined to the island of Tasmania off the southern coast of Australia, the name devil' was given to these creatures by the early European settlers, who found them highly aggressive and noisy. Tasmanian devils were also disliked because they killed poultry. They fill a role as a predator equivalent to small wild cats in other parts of the world.

The last apes in Europe

The Barbary ape is the only monkey found in Europe, retaining a tenuous foothold in Gibraltar. But it appears that these apes are not native to the peninsula, although they have certainly been resident there since the early 700s. Since then, the colony has been maintained by importations of Barbary apes from North Africa. Their presence has assumed a strategic importance down the years. During the Second World War, the British Prime Minister, Winston Churchill, even insisted that more of these apes were brought over from North Africa to dispel the long-held belief that the British hold on this strategic entry point to the Mediterranean will vanish when the apes die out.

Living oil wells

Elephant seals may range as far as 4,827km(3,000 miles) from their birthplace. These are the largest of all seals and were nearly eliminated by severe hunting during the last century. However, unlike many seals they were not persecuted for their pelts but rather for their fat stores. There is enough blubber on each seal to make about 363 litres (80 gallons) of oil. This layer of fat, which can be as much as 15cm(6in) thick in parts, helps to insulate these animals against the cold waters in which they live.

New discoveries

The okapi is just one of the larger mammals discovered during the twentieth century. Others include lemurs and, most recently, the onza - a wild cat that occurs in Central America.

Bright eyes

Most mammals that hunt at night have a mirrorlike layer of crystals at the back of the eye that reflect the small amounts of available light back through the retina to 'fire' the light-sensitive cells a second time to increase their night vision. This reflective layer - the tapetum - shines when these animals - such as cats and foxes - are caught in vehicle headlights.

Cracking good stuff

Mongooses relish eggs and have three ways to crack open the shell. The water mongoose picks up the egg in its front paws, stands up on its hind legs and throws the egg down onto the ground. The banded mongoose throws the egg backwards

through its hind legs at a suitable rock, and the Madagascan mongoose rolls onto its back and hurls the egg at a rock using all four feet.

The smallest cetacean
At a maximum length of 1.5m (4.9ft), the vaquita is probably the smallest cetacean (the group name for whales, dolphins and porpoises) in the world. This little-known porpoise lives in the upper Gulf of California.

Circling the wagons
Pioneers of the Wild West did not invent the strategy of circling the wagons to ward off intruders. Some mammals use this technique to protect their youngsters from threat. In the tundra areas of North America and Greenland, musk oxen live in herds of 100 individuals and if threatened form a circle, with their horned heads facing outwards, ready to repulse any attack from wolves, bears and other predators. The younger, more vulnerable members of the group stay safely within the circle. Elephants also form a similar protective circle around their calves.

Coyote con trick
Coyotes have been seen to 'play dead' and leap into savage life once they are surrounded by scavenging animals investigating 'the carcass'. They simply cannot run or fly away in time after the coyote's remarkable recovery.

The deepest diver
Whales can dive down to great depths in the ocean without suffering the 'bends' (decompression sickness caused by dissolved nitrogen bubbling out of the blood). In fact, their lungs collapse below about 100m (330ft). Sperm whales can certainly dive to a depth of 1,100m (3,600ft), but evidence suggests that they can dive down to 3,200m (10,500ft). Adult males can stay submerged for up to 90 minutes during a dive.

Domesticated but turning wild
The water buffalo is thought to have been domesticated over 5,000 years ago, in the vicinity of Indochina. It has since been introduced to a wide range of other areas and feral populations of water buffaloes (i.e. running wild from domesticated stock) are causing serious environmental damage in some countries, notably Australia. The horns of the domestic form are smaller than those of the wild buffalo.

The mammalian hairbrush
Adult hedgehogs have 5,000 spines. To prevent damage to the birth canal, the initial spines present in a newborn hedgehog are protected by a layer of skin, but they pop through in a matter of hours.

Air-attack cats
The serval and desert lynx are two long-legged cats that can pluck birds out of the sky. They rear up with lightning speed and clasp a bird with the front paws just after it takes off from the ground.

The biggest land mammal
The biggest African elephant ever known was a gigantic bull that weighed about 12.25 tonnes (just over 27,000lb) and stood more than 4m (13.1ft) tall at the shoulder. It was shot during 1974 in Angola, southern Africa.

The floating anvil
The sea otters living off the Californian coast use stones to crack open the shell of abalone - a marine mollusc that forms a major part of their diet. The otters float on their backs and place a large stone on their chests and use it like an anvil to smash the hard shells in order to liberate the succulent tissue inside. They will also use the stone to scrape off the sharp spines of sea urchins.

High-living mammals
Among the highest-living of all mammals is the large-eared pika of Nepal, a small rabbitlike mammal that flourishes at altitudes up to 6,100m (20,000 ft) in the Himalayas. It is active only during the middle part of the day.

Sonar sensing
Dolphins, porpoises and toothed whales can detect objects by using a sonar system in which 'clicks' of sound produced in the nasal passage are focused into a beam by a pad of fatty tissue on the forehead (the melon) and the echoes received through the lower jaw are conducted to the inner ear. Tests show that a blindfolded dolphin can distinguish between a solid and a hollow ball of the same size.

SUPERFACTS

Crabeaters that don't eat crabs

Despite its name, the crabeater seal does not eat crabs. This antarctic seal feeds mainly on krill, the planktonic crustaceans that swarm in the rich southern waters. The teeth that look so menacing are used simply as filters. The seal takes in a mouthful of krill and water and brings the jaws together so that the upper and lower teeth loosely interlock. Then, by pushing out the water through the 'mesh' formed by its teeth, the seal ends up with a generous portion of krill, which it swallows.

Mouse kills elephant

There is no truth in the story that elephants are terrified of mice, but a mouse is believed to have killed two elephants on one occasion. The incident occurred in the Queen Elizabeth Park, Uganda. A female elephant is thought to have accidentally sucked up a mouse and the rodent became lodged in her trunk. She then battered her trunk against a tree to dislodge it, but this proved unsuccessful. The cow finally collapsed from a fatal haemorrhage, crushing a young calf at the same time.

The magnificent mouflon

The mouflon is one of six species of wild sheep that have adapted to live in relatively inhospitable areas of the world. Native to Asia and introduced to Europe, the mouflon flourishes in cold and desert habitats. As in all wild sheep, the horns are used as battering rams in fights, which can be long but are more ritualistic than damaging. In the wild sheep found in the Altai Mountains of northwest China and western Mongolia, the horns of the males may weigh 22kg(48.5lb) or more, representing up to 13 percent of their total body weight.

Bat radar

Bats really do have some sophisticated radar equipment. As the greater horseshoe bat homes in on its prey, the pulses of sound change from 10 per second in a wide beam in stages up to a narrow sound beam of 75 pulses per second to create a more detailed echo picture of the flying insect in its sights.

Ice-toppling killer whales

Killer whales have been seen to coordinate their efforts to topple seals from ice floes. Having spotted a seal on a small ice floe, one whale will leap out of the water onto the side of the floe so that it topples sideways, giving the seal no alternative but to slide into the jaws of the other killer whales gathered round.

Unicorns of the sea

The single tusk of the narwhal can reach up to 3m(10ft) long and always has a lefthanded spiral when viewed from the root. The tusk, usually only found in males, is formed from an upper left tooth that grows forwards through the lip. Rarely, there are two tusks.

A is for aardvark

The aardvark is always one of the first entries in every dictionary and a more curious-looking beast is hard to imagine. With its long ears, heavily built snout and back legs and tail like a small kangaroo, the aardvark (the name literally means 'earth pig') breaks into termite mounds and licks up the hordes of insects as they swarm out to attack the intruder. A filter of stiff bristles keep the termites from going up the aardvark's nose.

Bubble-blowing whales
Humpback whales can concentrate shoals of fish by

Long-distance gliders
Large flying squirrels can glide a distance of 100m(330ft) from branch to branch. The scaly-tailed flying squirrels - some very small and all only distantly related to true squirrels - can glide for twice this distance.

cats can purr but cannot roar. The jaguar (*Panthera onca*), is classified as a big cat, even though it coughs or grunts rather than roars. On the other hand, the puma (also known as the mountain lion or cougar), which because of its large size would seem to be a big cat, is classified as a small one

living relatives. Fossil, anatomical and biochemical evidence confirm that together with the sea cows - represented today by manatees and dugongs - hyraxes are indeed related to the extinct mastodons, mammoths and the Asian and African elephant. Both groups have a relatively long gestation period: in hyraxes it is 7-8 months; in elephants, it is typically 22 months.

blowing a curtain of bubbles around them from below and then bursting up through the centre with their mouths open to engulf the surrounded prey.

Time to get up
Marmots may remain dormant for up to eight months of the year in the far north of their range - longer than any other mammal. During their hibernation, their breathing rate, heartbeat and temperature drop dramatically.

Magnetic navigation
Some whales and dolphins have crystals of magnetite, a natural substance sensitive to magnetism, in their skulls and they use these 'on-board compasses' to follow lines of magnetic force in the oceans. This could explain how they navigate in the open sea and also why they sometimes strand on

coastlines that cut directly across these unseen lines of force.

The prolific red bat
Whereas most bats bear one offspring and some bear twins, the red bat of North America may bear up to four babies in one litter. To cope with the demand for milk, the red bat is unique in having four nipples. These insectivorous bats are difficult to spot during the daytime, when they roost out of sight in trees. To avoid the worst of the winter weather, they tend to migrate southwards in search of new supplies of insects. Where they do hibernate, red bats have been known to survive a body temperature of -5°C(23°F).

Big cats roar, small cats purr
It is difficult to distinguish between the big cats (genus *Panthera*) and the small cats (genus *Felis*) purely on relative size. A useful difference between them, however, is that big cats can roar but cannot purr, while the small

(*Felis concolor*) because it purrs and screams but does not roar.

The humble hyrax - one of the elephant's closest relatives
Hyraxes, or conies, are rabbit-sized mammals that live among rocks or trees in Africa and the Middle East. Surprisingly, they are one of the elephant's closest

The influence of man
Left to its own devices, evolution is normally a very slow process, taking place over hundreds of thousands if not millions of years. With the arrival of man on the scene, comparatively recently in evolutionary terms, the pace of change has stepped up a gear. It is a sobering thought that man, the world's dominant mammal, has become the most important factor in the survival of many species that share the planet. Indeed, over 80 different species of his fellow mammals have become extinct during the last 400 years, largely as a result of human interference in their environment or because of direct persecution. Many others, such as the blue whale, are under threat. Even so, new species of mammals are still being discovered.

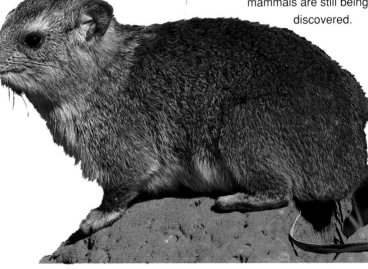

In the bleak tundra of Baffin Island, off the northeastern coast of Canada, a lone wolf howls to keep in touch with other members of its pack.

Once they leave their family herd, African bull elephants lead a fairly solitary life, only seeking company in male groups or when they find a receptive female. Dominant males achieve their status by fights and 'trials of strength'.

PICTURE CREDITS

The publishers wish to thank the following photographers and agencies who have supplied photographs for this book. The photographers have been credited by page number and position on the page: (B)Bottom, (T)Top, (C)Centre, (BL)Bottom Left, etc.

Bruce Coleman Limited: 98-9(T, Ken Balcomb)

Frank Lane Picture Agency:
Ron Austing: 99(B)
C. Carvalho: 28(B), 77(BR), 102(T)
Hugh Clark: 20-1(C), 45(B)
Tom & Pam Gardner: 16-17(BC), 25(TL)
Tony Hamblin: 95(T)
F. Hartmann: 31(B), 79(CR)
David Hosking: 37(B), 43(B), 47(TR), 62
Eric Hosking: 63(TR)
Eric & David Hosking: 22(TL), 98(B)
Carlo Dani Ingrid Jeske: 19(TR)
Siegfried Kerscher: 10(CR), 60(T)
Frank Lane: 11(B), 26(TL), 27(TL), 32(T), 43(C), 53(TR), 61(CR), 84-5(TC), 86-7(C), 91(BC)
S. McCutcheon: 10(CR), 60(T)
Mark Newman: 8-9, 17(TL), 34(B), 49(TC,TR), 67(T)
R. van Nostrand: 21(BR), 53(B), 89(TC)
Philip Perry: 46-7(TC), 56(T), 74(TR)
Fritz Polking: 59(TC), 72-3(TC), 103(B)
K.G. Preston-Mafham: 64(T)
Mandal Ranjit: 6-7
Leonard Lee Rue III: 48(TL), 75(T)
A.N.T. Schnabeltier: 17(TL)
Silvestris: 41(TR), 57(TC)
John Tinning: 23(TR)
R.S. Virdee: 72-3(B)
Terry Whittaker: 35(B), 36(T), 42(T), 55(T), 66-7(C), 89(CR), 93(TR), 101
W. Wisniewski: 19(TC), 21(TR), 59(TL), 77(TL), 83(BR), 88-9(C), Back endpaper
Martin B. Withers: 42-3(C), 64-5(C)

Konrad Wothe: 90(T)

Natural Science Photos:
C. Banks: 17(BR), 87(B)
C. Blaney: 41(B)
Ken Cole: 54(B), 83(TR), 100(T)
B. Gibbs: 13(BR,TR), 68-9(C), 70(B)
M. Harvey: 86(B)
Lex Hes: 71, 94
C. Jones: 95(C), 106
Paul Kay: 52
G. Kinns: 12-13(T), 61(L)
J.C. Pasieka: 15(TR)
C & T. Stuart: 10(CL), 12(T), 79(T)
A. Ward: 19(BC)
Kennan Ward: 77(BL, TR), 93(B)
P.H. & S.L. Ward: 11(T), 14(BR)
John W. Warden: 15(TL), 50-1(BC)

Photo Researchers Inc.:
Nick Bergkessel: 47(TL)
Marcello Bertinetti: 91(TR)
E. Brewer: 33(CR)
Scott Camazine: 23(TL), 78(T)
Larry Cameron: 27(B)
William Curtsinger:53(C), 76
Tim Davis: 97(L)
Gregory Dimijian: Front endpaper, 65(T), 68(B), 82-3(TC)
Phil A. Dotson: 63(TL), 92
Robert J. Erwin: 56-7(C)
Douglas Faulkner: 80, 81
Kenneth W. Fink: 28-9(T)
Francois Gohier: 38-9(TC), 50(BL), 51(T,B), 84-5(C)
Robert W. Hernandez: 27(TR)
George Holton: 57(CR), 91(TL), 95(B)
G.C. Kelley: 40-1(C), 63(B)

Stephen J. Krasemann: 10-11(CT), 25(TR), 31(T), 69(B), 82-3(BC)
Pat & Tom Leeson: 41(TC), 44-5(TC), 46-7(BC)
Renee Lynn: 69(T)
Leonard Lee Rue III: 22-3(B), 48-9(C), 54-5(C), 93(CL), 97(TR)
James M. McCann: 58-9(C)
Tom McHugh: 13(BL), 19(TL), 20(TL), 23(TC), 26-7(C), 29(B,TR), 32-3(C), 33(T,BR), 34-5(T), 35(T), 37(T), 38(B), 43(T), 44(B), 55(B), 58(T), 59(CR), 70-1(C), 74(BL), 74-5(C), 84(BL), 85(TR), 88(TL), 90-1(C), 96(B), 105
Mark D. Phillips: 30-1(C)
Rod Planck: 100(B)
E. Hanumantha Rao: 67(B)
M. Reardon: 4-5, 96-7(C)
Gary Retherford: 39(C)
Alan Root: 88(TR)
Jany Sauvanet: 29(TC), 38-9(C)
T. Segal: 30(L)
C. Seghers II: 14(BL), 18-19(BC)
St. Meyers/Okapia: 102(B)
Merlin D. Tuttle/Bat Conservation International: 24(TR), 24-5(C), 25(B), 103(T)
H. Uible: 23(C)
Stan Wayman: 39(CR)
David Weintraub: 73(TR)
Helen Williams: 36-7(C)

Artwork on pages 98-99 prepared by Glenn Smith.

A colony of northern fur seals in Alaska, where male rivalry dominates the breeding season.